EXERCISES IN
METEOROLOGY

SECOND EDITION

EXERCISES IN
METEOROLOGY

SECOND EDITION

ROBERT A. PAUL

Northern Essex Community College
Haverhill, Massachusetts

PRENTICE HALL, UPPER SADDLE RIVER, NJ 07458

To my family—
my wife Phyllis; Bob, Andrea, and Rick

Acquisitions Editor: Robert A. McConnin
Assistant Vice President and Director of Production: David W. Riccardi
Total Concept Coordinator: Kimberly P. Karpovich
Special Projects Manager: Barbara A. Murray
Production Editorial/Composition: ECL Art
Cover Design: Bruce Kenselaar
Cover Photo: Rick Schmidt/Weatherwise Photography Contest

Printed in the United States of America

10   9   8   7   6

ISBN 0-02-393212-0

Prentice-Hall International (UK) Limited, *London*
Prentice-Hall of Australia Pty. Limited, *Sydney*
Prentice-Hall Canada Inc., *Toronto*
Prentice-Hall Hispanoamericana, S.A., *Mexico*
Prentice-Hall of India Private Limited, *New Delhi*
Prentice-Hall of Japan, Inc., *Tokyo*
Prentice-Hall Asia Pte. Ltd., *Singapore*
Editora Prentice-Hall do Brasil, Ltda., *Rio de Janeiro*

CONTENTS

List of Tables in *Appendix A*

Extra Work Maps in *Appendix B*

DETAILED CONTENTS

PREFACE

To the Instructor

This manual may be used in any introductory meteorology course, with or without a separate laboratory session. Although this manual follows closely the ideas and concepts found in most standard textbooks (such as those listed at the end of this preface), it does not attempt to follow precisely the particular content and organization of any one book. The sequence of chapters may be altered or the exercises regrouped to suit your instructional approach. Exercises that deal with long-term data, for instance, appear in several chapters but could be regrouped to be used with the chapter on climate. Exercises dealing with weather map symbols, also found in several chapters, could be regrouped for use with Chapter 11, The Weather Map. Some exercises may be skipped or assigned for extra credit.

Please keep in mind the following general characteristics of this manual as guides to its intended use:

1. I have included more exercises here than I expect most instructors to use. The quantity and variety of these exercises should allow you ample choice.

2. Exercises vary in difficulty and the time required to do them. This should accommodate different levels of students as well as different amounts of available time.

3. Some types of exercises, especially those that require practice and the development of skills (in computation, data handling, map analysis, plotting and graphing, etc.), appear so often they may seem repetitious. Their frequent reappearance is intentional and gives you the choice of:

    a. limiting the number of problems to be solved,

    b. assigning more work as homework,

    c. requiring that additional exercises of the same type be done only by those students who *need* the extra practice,

      or

    d. spreading out added exercises over the length of the course to keep the students in practice. (This is usually more beneficial than doing similar exercises all at one time, which is mere repetition.)

4. In courses with separate laboratory sessions, a proven technique has been to assign some of the shorter and more self-directed exercises as homework in preparation for the lab. The lab session then begins with a review and discussion of those exercises, followed by one of the more involved exercises for the students to work on during the lab session.

5. This manual presents material on such popular topics as air pollution and severe storms within chapters about more general topics, rather than in separate chapters. For example, several exercises on temperature inversions, lapse rates, and atmospheric stability relate well to the air pollution issue. Questions about acid rain and about the use of a radar summary map in assessing the potential for severe weather are found in Chapter 8, Moisture in the Atmosphere. Cyclonic storms and thunderstorms are the subjects of exercises in several chapters, and exercises dealing with their structure are included in Chapter 10, Air Masses, Fronts, and Severe Storms. Two upper-air maps (500 mb) may be found in Chapter 12, Weather Analysis and Forecasting.

6. Work with weather maps should start early and continue throughout the course. An ample group of exercises related to maps appears in Chapter 11, The Weather Map, and Chapter 12, Weather Analysis and Forecasting. These exercises should be apportioned throughout the course to provide the student with frequent practice. A few additional insights into working with these maps are provided in the section of this preface addressed to the student.

7. Several extra blank work maps are provided in Appendix B. These may be used in any way you wish.

AN INVITATION TO ALL INSTRUCTORS

Your comments, suggestions, and ideas are actively sought. I would like to know which exercises you like, which exercises you find unsatisfactory, and what you would like to have added. If you have any favorite exercises of your own, I would be pleased to consider them for inclusion in a future edition of this manual (with your contribution properly acknowledged). Please send a preliminary draft to me at Northern Essex Community College, Elliott Way, Haverhill, MA 01830. You may also initiate discussion of your ideas via the Internet to: rpaul@mecn.mass.edu

To the Student

This manual is compatible with most standard meteorology textbooks. No matter what text you are using, always review the appropriate material in it before doing the exercises in this manual. By studying related illustrations in your textbook, you can often get a preliminary grasp of what your graph or map in an exercise should look like. This is particularly helpful in getting a feel for the effects that a graph's scale can have on the smoothness or irregularity of a curve plotted on it and for the contours of the many kinds of isopleths you will draw on weather maps.

Meteorology in the United States employs a combination of English and metric units. English units predominate in synoptic meteorology on land, and most weather information given to the public is in English units. Metric units are used in marine meteorology, most branches of atmospheric research, and in scholarly work. Many opportunities to compare the two systems and to practice converting from one system to the other are provided in this manual.

Appendix A contains tables of information necessary in completing the exercises or useful for general reference (such as conversion factors and SI units). Tables needed for the exercises are referred to in the appropriate chapters (all numbered tables referred to in this manual can be found in Appendix A), but you should become familiar with *all* the tables and the information they provide.

Keep in mind that such areas of meteorology as finding and plotting fronts from weather data, projecting the path of a storm, and forecasting weather in general are as much an art as a science. You should not expect to do as perfect job in your first attempts. Always remember: even professional forecasters make their share of mistakes!

Acknowledgments

The author wishes to acknowledge the helpful comments and suggestions from the following reviewers: Stephen Berman, SUNY College Oneonta; Mark McConnaughhay, Dutchess County Community College; Lawrence L. Moses, California University of Pennsylvania; and Steven B. Newman, Central Connecticut State University. In addition, the guidance and advice of my editor, Bob McConnin, Executive Editor at Prentice Hall, is deeply appreciated.

Compatible Textbooks

Ahrens, C.D. *Meteorology Today: An Introduction to Weather, Climate, and the Environment.* 5th ed., St. Paul: West Publishing Co., 1994.

Ahrens, C.D. *Essentials of Meteorology: An Invitation to the Atmosphere.* St. Paul: West Publishing Co., 1992.

Athens, R.A. *Meteorology.* 6th ed., New York: Macmillan Publishing Co., 1992.

Barry, R.G., and R.J. Chorley. *Atmosphere, Weather & Climate.* 5th ed., New York: Routledge, 1993.

Hidore, J.J. and J.E. Oliver *Climatology: An Atmospheric Science.* New York: Macmillan Publishing Co., 1993.

Lutgens, F.K., and E.J. Tarbuck. *The Atmosphere: An Introduction to Meteorology.* 6th ed., Englewood Cliffs, N.J.: Prentice-Hall, 1995

Lydolph, P.E. *Weather and Climate.* Totowa, N.J.: Rowman & Allanheld, 1985.

————. *The Climate of the Earth.* Totowa, N.J.: Rowman & Allanheld, 1985.

Moran, J.M., and M.D. Morgan. *Meteorology: The Atmosphere and the Science of Weather.* 4th ed., New York: Macmillan Publishing Co., 1994.

————. *Essentials of Weather.* Englewood Cliffs, N.J.: Prentice-Hall, 1995.

chapter **1** ⎯⎯⎯⎯⎯⎯⎯⎯⎯⎯⎯⎯⎯⎯⎯⎯⎯⎯⎯⎯⎯⎯

INTRODUCTION TO WEATHER and ISOPLETHS

Although weather and climate are separate concepts, they are inextricably related. Either one may help to explain or describe the other. Either one may partially cause the other. The elements of weather are the elements of climate as well. Although this manual emphasizes the meteorological aspects of these elements, their climatic aspects will be considered as well.

A general consideration of the nature of the atmosphere (Chapter 2) introduces the gaseous environment within which meteorological and climatological processes take place. A close look at the ways in which the earth is physically related to the sun—relationships that are fundamental to most processes of weather and climate—then follows (Chapter 3). Such relationships explain what happens when solar radiation is received at the outer atmosphere, passes through the earth's atmosphere, and reaches the surface of the earth (Chapter 4). Solar radiation provides the energy that becomes manifest as differences in temperature in air, land, and water. These temperature differences (Chapter 5) help to explain some of the major differences in atmospheric pressure (Chapter 6). Wind and the general circulation of the atmosphere (Chapter 7) are largely consequences of these pressure and temperature patterns. Solar radiation also provides energy for the evaporation process and the hydrologic cycle. An understanding of these processes and other aspects of moisture in the atmosphere (Chapter 8) provides the basis for an examination of adiabatic processes and the question of atmospheric stability and instability (Chapter 9).

An air mass (Chapter 10) contains all the elements of weather (temperature, pressure, wind flow, moisture, sky cover, etc.) and may explain the weather and its changes. The air mass concept may also help to explain the climate in areas dominated throughout most of the year by a given type of air mass. The boundaries between air masses are the weather fronts (Chapter 10), which produce interesting sequences of changes in the weather when they pass through an area.

The phenomena of weather are observed, measured, and reported by an extensive network of weather stations. The data thus collected are computerized, summarized, expanded, contracted, modified, extracted, analyzed, prognosticated from, and otherwise manipulated in innumerable ways to produce a large variety of weather maps and charts (Chapter 11). The most basic of these, the surface analysis weather map, embodies the fundamental synoptic (symbolic) language of meteorology.

One of the most significant purposes of the study of meteorological processes, weather conditions, and the weather map is to be able to forecast future weather conditions (Chapter 12). An understanding of the individual processes and elements of the atmosphere and its weather, treated in the early chapters of this manual, is the basis for the analysis and forecasting of weather discussed in Chapter 12.

With many of the longer-term aspects of atmospheric elements introduced along the way in each chapter, it remains to summarize these elements from the climatic point of view. Chapter 13 provides this summary of world climates and introduces one widely used system for analyzing and describing climatic data and identifying the climate regions of the world.

Because the study of weather maps should begin early, this introductory chapter presents an explanation of **isopleths**—various kinds of lines drawn on maps to depict the pattern of weather data and to aid in the analysis of that information. These lines, once drawn, are very easy to understand. The problem is in discerning, from the confusion of data plotted on a map, where they should be drawn.

The simple exercises at the end of this chapter provide an introduction to the concept of the isopleth and some practice in drawing isopleths for highly simplified and abstract values. Following these abstract exercises, a map with a very simple isothermal pattern is given. This is followed by a map with a more complex pattern including a "temperature anomaly" in the southeast (Exercise 1.6). Lastly, an exercise in "guesstimation" is provided in order to introduce the weather elements and emphasize the need for accurate measurement and precise definition of weather phenomena. The simple exercises dealing with isopleths should help to pave the way for handling more complex situations that will be found in subsequent chapters. In each chapter where an exercise requires the drawing of some type of isopleth, it may prove helpful to come back and restudy the following information about isopleths.

The Nature of Isopleths

Isopleths are lines that connect all the places on a map to which the same numerical value of some measurement applies. (The Greek *iso* means equal.) Such lines separate higher values from lower values. They also show the area or distance between values. The terms **isopleth, isarithm,** and **isoline** are all general terms for lines of equal quantitative value and are often used synonymously. *Isopleth* is the preferred term, although some purists restrict its use to cases in which values are ratios representing a quantity per unit (such as rainfall per hour or snow depth per square mile). "Isarithm" then applies to lines of a simple numerical value and "isoline" becomes a generic term encompassing both isopleths and isarithms. However, in ordinary usage, isopleth is the umbrella term for any line of equal value.

Because of the great variety of data that may be plotted by such lines, specific names are given to various kinds of isopleths, such as **isobars** (lines of equal barometric pressure), **isotherms** (lines of equal temperature value), and **isohyets** (lines of equal precipitation amounts). Even among these types of isopleths

there are subtypes. An isothermal map, for example, might show the temperature pattern at a given moment, the pattern of maximum temperatures for a given day, or the pattern of average temperatures for a month or a year. Isotherms may apply to data for soil or water as well as for air. As many different types of isotherms may be used as there are different types of temperature data. The same idea applies to all other kinds of isopleths. To know exactly what an isopleth map is depicting, read the map title and legend carefully before studying the isopleth pattern.

The following are some common (and some not-so-common) types and subtypes of isopleths:

isobar (*baros* = weight)—equal barometric pressure
    isallobar—equal pressure change per unit of time
isotherm (*therme* = heat)—equal temperature
    isochein—equal mean winter temperature
    isothere—equal mean summer temperature
    isophytochrone—equally long growing season
    isotalantose—equal range of mean warmest and mean coldest months
    isocryme—equal lowest mean temperature
isohyet (*hyetos* = rain)—equal precipitaion
    isomer—equal mean monthly rainfall
    isohyomene—equal wet months
    isonif—equal snowfall
    isothermombrose—equal summer rainfall
isoryme—equal frost incidence
isohel—equal degree of sunshine
isoneph—equal amounts of cloudiness
isokeraun—equal thunderstorm frequency

Many other such terms exist, especially from the related earth sciences: *isohypse* (elevation); *isobath* (depth of water); *isogone* (magnetic declination); *isohaline* (salinity of water); *isochron* (time); *isotach* (fluid velocity); *isophenomenal* (equal phenomena of any kind, useful with qualitative data!); and many more.

Isopleths have some interesting characteristics that may be expressed as "rules":

1. Isopleths are drawn precisely *through* a specific place only if the data for that place has the *exact* value of that isopleth.

2. Isopleths have a higher-value side and a lower-value side. That is, the area on one side of an isopleth encompasses values that are higher than the exact value of the isopleth and the area on the other side encompasses values that are lower.

3. All higher (or lower) values in the immediate vicinity of an isopleth should be on the same side of the line.

4. Isopleth values always have a uniform interval.

5. Isopleths must be drawn for all values between the highest and lowest, according to the interval used, even if the actual data is missing for some isopleth values.

6. The spacing of isopleths is governed by the actual data. Considerable interpolation is necessary for the placement of lines between known values. Such interpolation is based upon the general pattern that emerges, but may be initiated by an assumption of equal spacing. The general pattern may show a *gradient* that subsequent isopleths should follow—until the general pattern changes.

7. The spacing of isopleths is an indication of the rate of change in values per unit of horizontal distance on the map. Wide spacing indicates gentle change while close spacing indicates rapid change. As will be seen, the spacing of isobars (for air pressure) indicates the speed of the wind.

8. Isopleths always form closed loops. Although a given map may not cover enough area to show the closure of an isopleth loop, world maps always show isopleths as closed loops.

9. Isopleths never cross each other.

10. More than one isopleth of the same value may appear within the area of the map. These may be separate isopleths with the same value, or a given isopleth may leave the area of the map and then reappear elsewhere on the map.

11. The values on a map may *reverse* their tendency to increase or decrease in a given map direction. (This is what necessitates more than one isopleth of the same value, as described in "rule" 10.)

12. Traversing two adjacent isopleths of the same value (with no other isopleths intervening) indicates a change in the *sequence* of the data from increasing values to decreasing values or vice versa.

Drawing Isopleths

At first, isopleths should always be drawn *lightly in pencil*. They will inevitably require correction, adjustment, and redrawing before their positions are finalized. Only after all of them have been drawn and the spacing has been adjusted should these lines be made darker or redone in ink.

The first step is to determine the interval to be used. The interval is determined by several factors such as the *range* of the data, the physical size of the map, and whether or not a standard practice exists. If a standard practice exists it should be followed. The 4 mb isobar interval used to show the pattern of air pressure on maps of the United States is an example. The individual isobars are multiples of 4 mb counting from 1000 mb. Thus, proper values include 992, 996, 1000, 1004, 1008, 1012, etc. To depart from a standard interval will make comparisons of several maps difficult and misleading. If a standard interval does not exist, then the interval value should be narrow (small) enough to show sufficient detail and to provide a clear pattern. At the same time, the interval should *not* be so narrow that it results in excessive lines crowded together cluttering the map and hiding other information on the map. On maps that show temperature patterns (isotherms), a 5° or 10° interval is somewhat standard, and the isotherms should be multiples of that interval counting from 0°. If it makes sense to use an interval of 10° F, then it should be 10°, 20°, 30°, rather than 5°, 15°, 25°.

The next step is establishing *which* isopleths must be drawn (or how many different values of isopleths must be drawn). The difference between the highest and lowest values shown in the data plotted on the map (the *range*), divided by the isopleth *interval* required or selected, gives the *approximate* number of different isopleth values that are needed. Since an isopleth of a given value may be needed more than once in other areas of the map you cannot, ahead of time, determine how many isopleths will be needed—only which values. If an interval of 4 mb is required for drawing isobars on a map, and data ranges from 995 mb to 1025 mb, then the difference (1025–995) is 30 mb. The quotient obtained by dividing this difference by the interval (30 ÷ 4) is *more than* 7. Thus, eight *differently valued* isobars must be drawn (the lowest being the 996 mb isobar and the highest being the 1024 mb isobar. Again, more than eight isobars may be drawn if a given value is needed more than once, but only eight differently valued isobars will be needed.

The most difficult task is to draw the first line—to get started. It is usually helpful to study and grasp the general pattern of the data before trying to draw the first line. Looking for an area with the highest values (or an area with the lowest values) may prove helpful. Once such an area is found, find the absolute highest (or lowest) value. Select the isopleth value, according to the required interval, that will encompass this extreme and leave all other values outside that first isopleth. It then becomes only a matter of adding more isopleths of higher (or lower) value outward from the first one. A pattern will usually emerge. Eventually, this pattern must break and a given iso-

pleth will no longer conform to the original pattern. This is normal.

It is also normal for most isopleths to be *smooth* lines. They should not have wiggles and bends unwarranted by the data. It is highly recommended that you examine the isobars on the many maps in Chapter 12 to get a mental picture of how such isobars look after they are finalized. Notice how they are smooth, gently curved as the data allows, and evenly spaced in areas where data is lacking. The only exception to the generalization that isopleths should have smooth curves rather than sharp points is when isobars cross weather fronts. Notice in the examples in Chapter 12 that isobars bend *sharply* when crossing a front.

Additional information about the proper labeling of isobars is found in the text in Chapter 12.

name   section   date

Exercises

DRAWING ISOPLETHS

The following simple exercises, followed by a map with actual temperature data, provide an opportunity to practice the basic skill of drawing isopleths that *separate* values as well as connect places with the same value. Similar exercises using other weather data are found in other chapters.

General Practice

1.1 Continue the line (an isopleth) that has been started for you in the box below. All *X*s must be on one side of the line and all *O*s on the other side. You must draw only *one continuous* line, which will form a closed loop within the box. (There is more than one way to solve this problem.)

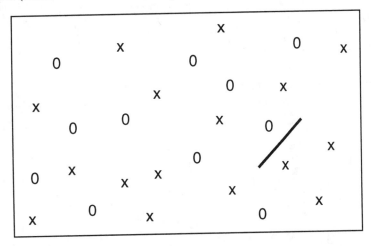

1.2 Try it again. This time draw your isopleth to separate the *K*s and *Z*s. And this time you may *start* your separating line *anywhere* you like. You must draw only one line, which will form a closed loop within the box.

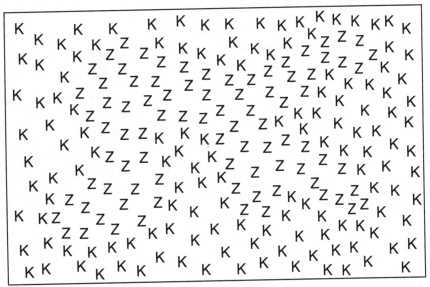

1.3   This time draw an isopleth that will separate the 6s and 7s. More than one line may be needed this time, and do not expect each line to form a closed loop within the "map" area.

```
7 7 7 7 7 7 7 7 7 7 7 7 7 7 7 7 7 7 7 7 7 7 7
 7 7 7 7 7 7 7 7 7 7 7 7 7 7 7 7 7 7 7 7 7 7 7
7 7 7 7 7 6 7 7 7 7 7 7 7 7 7 7 6 7 7 7 7 7 7
 7 7 7 7 6 6 7 7 7 7 7 7 7 7 6 6 6 7 7 7 7 7
7 7 7 7 6 6 6   7 7 7 7 7 6 6 6 7 7 7 7 7
 6 6  6 6 6 6  6 6 6 6  6 6 6 6  6 6 6 6 7 7 7 7
 6 6  6 6 6 6 6 6 6 6 7 7 7 7  6 6 6 6 7 7 7 7
 6 6 7 7 7 7 7 7 7 7 7 7 7 7 7 6 6 6 6 7 7 7 7
6 6 7 7 7 7 7 7 7 7 7 7 7 7 7 7 6 6 6 7 7 7 7
 6 6 7 7 7 7 7 7 7 7 7 7 7 7 7 6 6 6 6 7 7 7 7
 6 6 7 7 7 7 7 7 7 7 7 7 7 7 7 6 6 6 6  7 7 7 7
 6 7 7 7 7 7 7 7 7 7 7 7 7 7 7 6 6 6 7 7 7 7
6 7 7 7 7 7 7 7 7 7 7 7 7 7 7 6 7 7 7 7 7
7 7 7 7 7 7 7 7 7 7 7 7 7 7 7 7 7 7 7 7 7 7
 7 7 7 7 7 7 7 7 7 7 7 7 7 7 7 7 7 7 7 7 7 6 6
```

1.4   In addition to separating areas of different values, isopleths also represent places of equal value (along the line itself). Draw the isopleths for the values of 2, 4, 6, and 8 for the data in the box below.

```
3 3 3 4 5  5   5   5  5  5  5 5 5  5 5 5 6 7  7   7 7
 3 3  4  5  5 5 5  5 5  5 5  5 5 5 6  7 7  7   7 8
3 3  4  5 5  5 4 4 4  4 5  5 5  5 5  6  7 7  7 8
 3 4  5 5 4  3   3   3 4  5 5 5  5 5 6 7  7 7 8 9
3 4 5  5 4 3 3 3  3 3 3 3  4 5  5 5 5 6 7  7 7 8 9 9
4 5  5 4  3 3  2 2 2  3  3  4 5  5 5 6  7  7 8  9 9 9 9
 5 5 5 4  3 3  2 1 1  2 3  3 4 5  5 5 6  7  7 8 9 9 9 9
5  5 4  3 3  3 2 1 1 1  2 3  3 4 5  5 6 7  7 8 9 9  9 9
5  5 4 3 3 3  3 3  3 3 3 4  5 5  5 6 7  7 8 9  9 9 9
5 5 4  3 3 3   3 3 3 3  4 4  5 5 5  5 6 7  7 7 8  8 8 8
5 5 4  3 3 3  3 3 3  4 4  4 5 5 5  5 6  7  7 7  7 7 7
5 5 4  4 4  3 4 4  4 5 5 5  5 6  6 7 7  7  7 7 7 7
5  5 5 5  5 5 5 5 5 5  5 6  5 6  6 7 7  7  7 7 7 6
5  5 5  5 6 6  7 7 7 7  7  7 7 7  7 7 6 6  5
5 5 5  6 7  7 7 7  7 7 7 7  7 7  7 6 6 5 5  4 4
5 5 5  6 7 7  7 7  6 6 6 6  6 5  5 4 4 3 3
5 5 5  5 6 6 6  6 5 5 5 5 5 5  5 4 3 2 2
5 5 5 5  5 5 5  5 5 5 5 5 5  5 4 4 3 2 1 1 1
```

name   section   date

Simple Isotherms

1.5   The following map shows a simple temperature pattern. First, you should visually scan the data to try to visualize the temperature pattern. Then draw the isotherms, using a 10°F interval. Remember that an isotherm of a certain value will go through a station circle only if that station reports *precisely* the value of the isotherm being drawn. Otherwise, that particular isotherm should be drawn to keep higher values on one side and lower values on the other.

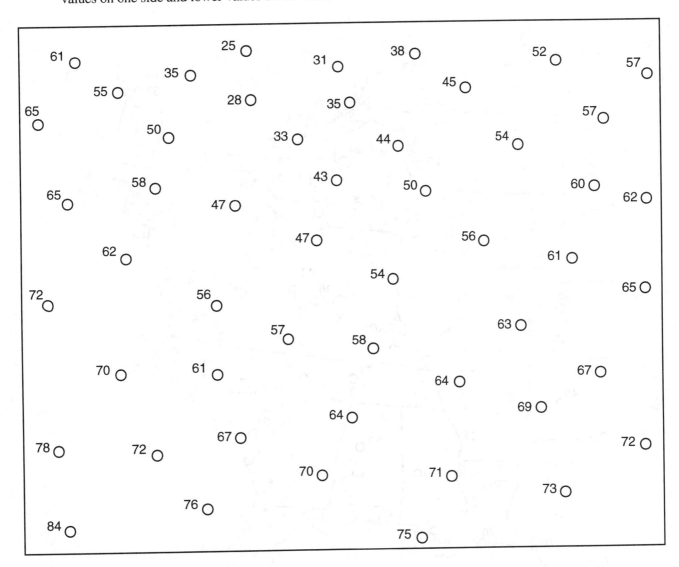

name   section   date

Isotherms

1.6   The following map shows the actual temperatures observed at 7:00 A.M. on a day in early April. Draw the necessary *isotherms* to show the temperature pattern at that time. Use a 10°F interval. Be sure to draw your isotherms *lightly in pencil* so that you may later eliminate unwarranted wiggles or kinks and poor spacing. Only when your isotherms are absolutely correct should you go over them to darken them. All isotherms should be labeled, and the labels should be kept in the same general region on the map, if possible.

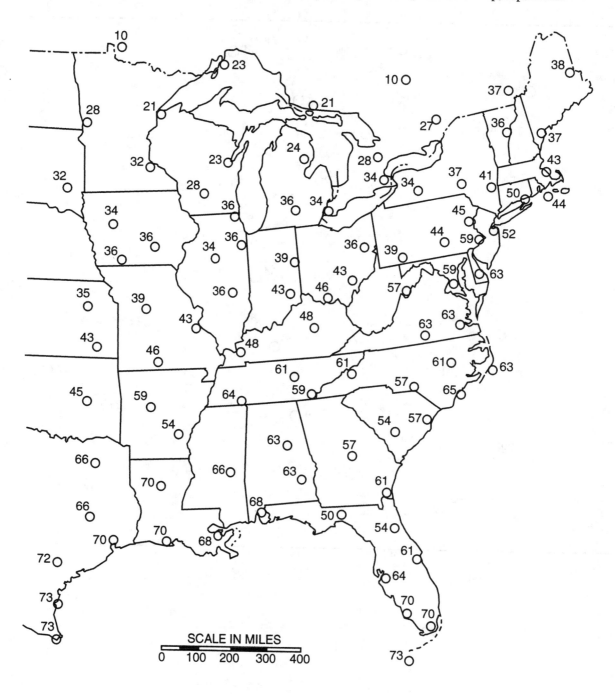

name   section   date

WEATHER ELEMENTS: OUTDOOR "GUESSTIMATION" EXERCISE

1.7   The purpose of this exercise (in addition to getting some fresh air!) is to discover the *need* for measuring instruments, the *need* to quantify, and the *need* to express clearly the *margin of error* in our observations.

You must go outdoors! No instruments are provided; in this exercise in "guesstimation" you can depend only on visual observations. Answer the following questions as well as you can, but do not expect to come up with exact data.

The following observations were made:

Place _____   Hour _____

Day and date _____

Significant Weather _____

a.   What is the wind direction? How did you determine this?

b.   What is the wind speed and how did you determine this?

c.   What is the air temperature? (Use *words*. Do *not* use numbers. Use subjective terminology in lieu of measuring instruments.)

d.   Now attempt to define the term or terms you have just used to describe the temperature.

e.   What is the air pressure? (What makes you think so?)

name   section   date

f.   What is the altitude of the sun (How many degrees of arc is the sun above the horizon)?

g.   What percentage of the sky is covered by clouds?

h.   How high is the base of the cloud nearest you?

i.   How many different types of clouds are in the sky?

j.   Describe the different types of clouds in the sky.

k.   How might you express, or label, your answers to the above questions in order to indicate their degree of "accuracy"?

name   section   date

Review and Study Questions

1. What is the difference between the concept of *weather* and the concept of *climate*?

2. How are weather and climate related?

3. **Climatic controls** are those factors that influence or help to determine the climate of a place. List the several major climatic controls below. Add anything else you think might be an important climatic control following *h*.

    a.

    b.

    c.

    d.

    e.

    f.

    g.

    h. Others:

4. Two of the climatic controls that should be in the above list are not only *controls* but also *elements* of weather and climate. Explain how each of these two weather elements helps to control or influence climate.

5.   What does the prefix *iso-* mean?

6.   List the three types of isopleths that are the most common in the study of weather and climate elements.

7.   What determines the spacing of isopleths on a map?

8.   What is indicated by a wide spacing of isopleths and what is indicated by a narrow (close) spacing of isopleths?

9.   In drawing isopleths (or in studying the information on an isopleth map), what is the *first fact* that must be clearly established? Why?

10.   How do the data determine the isopleth *interval* that should be used on a map?

chapter 2

THE ATMOSPHERE

The atmosphere is a thin envelope of gases that surrounds the earth. It is held to the earth by the force of gravity, and it moves with the earth as the earth rotates. The atmosphere also has motion of its own, relative to the earth's surface, called circulation. This general circulation and the many smaller-scale motions within it allow energy to pass from regions of surplus (the tropics) to regions of deficit (the polar regions).

The atmosphere has many different qualities and characteristics at different altitudes. It varies in temperature, pressure, density, and gaseous composition at various heights above the earth's surface. It contains regions of mixed gases and regions of relatively singular gases. It has regions of strong ionization, regions of pronounced magnetic forces, regions of entrapped radiation particles, and a region of molecular escape from earth's gravity. Based upon these differences, a regionalization is possible in which the atmosphere may be divided into individual spheres (or layers).

The entire atmosphere may be regionalized on the basis of a temperature criterion to produce such zones as the troposphere, stratosphere, mesosphere, and thermosphere—each with its own thermal properties. Or, if atmospheric composition is the criterion, the atmosphere may be divided into layers such as the homosphere and heterosphere (with its several sublayers). This produces overlap, so a given region of the atmosphere may be described by more than one name. In addition, other layers of the atmosphere are defined in terms of other criteria, and such regions as the ionosphere, magnetosphere, chemosphere, and exosphere are recognized. This causes still more overlap of the atmospheric regions. The initial confusion, however, is easily dispelled. The proper term to use in describing a given region of the atmosphere is the term that refers to the atmospheric characteristic that is of concern.

An interesting question is: Just how far from the earth's surface does the atmosphere extend? It is a rather academic question, and the answer depends on which definition of the atmosphere is used. If the atmosphere is defined in terms of its density, should the atmosphere be considered significant even at 20 mi up, where the density is less than 1% of what it is at the earth's surface? If it is defined by the earth's hold on atmospheric gases, then 6000 mi—the point at which significant numbers of molecules can escape the earth's gravitational attraction and join with interplanetary gases—may be an acceptable limit to the atmosphere. If the farthest limit of entrapped particles is used as a definition, then 16,000 mi is the answer. And, if the farthest extent to which the earth's magnetic field influences the behavior of charged particles is used as the definition, then the earth's atmosphere may be said to extend some 35,000 mi on the sun side of the earth and hundreds of thousands of miles on the other side.

The several answers to the original question define limits, and suggest vast areas, that are of importance to a total understanding of the earth's atmosphere. Such extensive areas are of special interest in the many fields of atmospheric science. Meteorology is only one of these sciences. Meteorology's primary concern is with the lowest 5 to 12 mi of the atmosphere—the troposphere. It is here that our weather takes place.

name   section   date

Review and Study Questions

1. Describe and explain the variations in the height of the **tropopause** (at different latitudes and different seasons).

2. What important wind is associated with the "breaks" in the position of the tropopause?

3. Describe the chemical composition of the atmosphere. (Give the percentages, by volume, of the four major gases.)

4. Describe the aerosols found in the atmosphere and their sources.

5. In spite of its relatively low molecular weight, water vapor is concentrated near the earth's surface. Explain this fact.

6. What is the role (or significance) of carbon dioxide in the atmosphere, what are its sources, and what is the significance of changing levels of CO_2 in the atmosphere?

7. What is the role of ozone in the atmosphere, what may be causing the amount of O_3 to change, and what may be the consequences of increasing or decreasing amounts of O_3 in the atmosphere?

8. Discuss the nature of the **ionosphere**: its location, its significance, and the process of its formation.

9. Describe the **magnetosphere**: its shape, location, and what it is.

10. Describe and discuss the **Van Allen radiation belts:** their location, composition, and significance.

11. How high does the earth's atmosphere extend? (Give more than one answer, with your justification for each answer. Which altitudinal figure do *you* prefer—and why?)

chapter **3**

EARTH–SUN RELATIONSHIPS

Temperature, air pressure, wind, humidity, precipitation, sky cover, and visibility describe the weather and climate of places on the earth's surface. These elements would not be what they are, nor would they change in the ways they do, if it were not for some very basic physical relationships between the earth and the sun. Recognition of such relationships is fundamental to an understanding of atmospheric processes, weather situations, and climatic conditions.

The sun provides nearly all the energy that powers atmospheric and oceanic circulations, that generates the geologic processes of weathering, erosion, transportation of materials, and deposition, and that supports and sustains life and growth within the biosphere.

The earth, with its elliptical orbit around the sun, rotates on an inclined axis and receives the sun's energy in a rhythmic pattern through time. Because of the inclination of the earth's axis and because the earth's axis at any point in the earth's orbit is parallel to the axis at any other such point, the most direct rays of the sun are shifted from north to south during the year (the declination of the sun). This declination brings about the seasons with their different intensities of solar radiation and varying lengths of daylight and darkness.

The surface of the earth receives its energy from the sun at an angle to its surface. For a given location, the angle varies during the year as well as during the daylight hours of a given day. For the same day or hour of the day, the angle will vary at different latitudes. This is of such importance in determining the amount of energy that may be received at various times and locations that the following section of this chapter is devoted to a more detailed explanation of sun angles. Chapter 4, Solar Radiation, is based in part on these same ideas of earth–sun relationships and sun angles.

Sun Angles

The angle at which the sun's rays strike the earth's surface is a major factor in the amount of energy received per unit of surface area. More direct rays provide more concentrated energy. More oblique rays spread the energy over a larger surface area and thus provide less energy per unit of surface area. Sun angles are also useful in navigation for determining a latitudinal position.

Study the diagrams in Figure 3.1.

FINDING THE ALTITUDE OF THE NOON SUN

To find out how many degrees above the horizon the sun will have risen by noon, follow two steps. First, find the arc, in degrees of latitude, between the observer and the sun's declination. (This is equal to the zenith angle of the observer.) If the observer and the sun's declination are both in the same hemisphere, the arc between them is found by subtraction. If the observer and the sun's declination are in different hemispheres, the arc between them is found by addition. The second step is to subtract the value of this arc from 90 degrees .

In the diagrams in Figure 3.1, the observer is located at 50 degrees N latitude and the sun's declination is 20 degrees S latitude. The *altitude angle* of the noon sun would be calculated as follows:

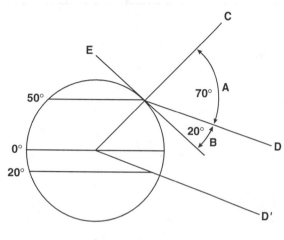

(a) GLOBAL VIEW

A = Zenith angle of observer.

A is also equal to the arc or distance (in degrees of latitude) between the observer and the sun's declination.

B = Altitude angle of sun.

C = Zenith of observer.

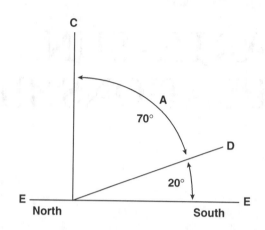

(b) CLOSE-UP OF OBSERVER'S HORIZON

D = Rays from the sun at 50° N.

D' = Rays from the sun at 20° S.
    D and D' are parallel.

D' = Sun's declination.

E = Horizon line of observer.

FIGURE 3.1   Sun Angle at 50° N.

Step 1:	*Step 2:*
50° N	90°
+20° S	−70°
70° arc in degrees of latitude or zenith angle	20° altitude angle of the sun

Step 1:	*Step 2:*
90°	70° zenith angle
−20° altitude angle	−20° declination
70° zenith angle	50° N latitude

Since the zenith angle and the declination are *both* south, the declination must be *subtracted* from the zenith angle.

FINDING THE LATITUDE OF YOUR LOCATION

For navigational purposes, as mentioned earlier, it is possible to determine latitudinal location from sun-angle relationships. A sextant is used to determine the angular altitude of the sun at local noon, and the tables in an almanac provide the sun's declination for every day. To find the *latitude*, first subtract the altitude angle from 90 degrees (which gives the observer's zenith angle). Then, if both the observer's zenith and the declination are north or if both are south, subtract this zenith angle from the declination. Otherwise, add the zenith angle to the declination.

In the diagrams in Figure 3.1, the noon altitude angle is 20 degrees and the declination is 20 degrees S. The *latitude* would be calculated as follows:

Example: Altitude angle for 75 degrees N on March 21.

(1)
$$\begin{array}{rl} 75° & N \\ -\ \ 0° & \text{declination (equator)} \\ \hline 75° & \end{array}$$

(2)
$$\begin{array}{rl} 90° & \\ -\ 75° & \\ \hline 15° & \text{altitude angle} \end{array}$$

Example: Latitude when noon altitude is 48.5 degrees on the northern horizon on December 22.

(1)
$$\begin{array}{rl} 90.0° & \\ 48.5° & \\ \hline 41.5° & \text{zenith angle} \end{array}$$

(2)
$$\begin{array}{rl} 41.5° & \\ +\ 23.5° & \text{declination} \\ \hline 65.0° & \text{S latitude} \end{array}$$

name   section   date

Exercises

3.1 Using the following diagram of the earth, answer the questions below in the spaces provided. Remember that the lines on the diagram may be circles on a true sphere.

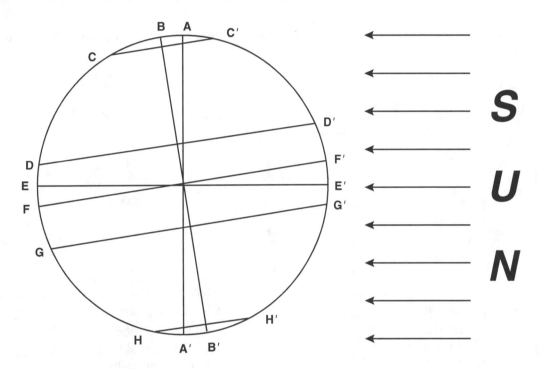

a. What is the name of line A–A′? _____

b. What is the name of line B–B′? _____

c. What is the name of line C–C′? _____

d. What is the name of line D–D′? _____

e. What is the name of line E–E′? _____

f. What is the name of line F–F′? _____

g. What is the name of line G–G′? _____

h. What is the name of line H–H′? _____

i. What is the arc, in degrees, between points F and G? _____

j. What is the arc, in degrees, between points D and G? _____

k. What is the arc, in degrees, between points C and D? _____

l. What is the arc, in degrees, between points B′ and H′? _____

m. What is the date (exact month and an approximate day) for the earth–sun relationship shown in the above diagram? _____

name   section   date

3.2   The earth, with its axis of rotation, is shown below at two different moments in its orbit around the sun. On *each* of these diagrams you are to

a.   Draw the equator, the Arctic and Antarctic Circles, and the Tropics of Cancer and Capricorn.

b.   Draw the Circle of Illumination and lightly shade the nighttime hemispheres.

c.   Add a short arrow pointing directly at the spot on the earth that is receiving the most direct rays from the sun.

d.   Place an *X* on each diagram where the upper-most and lower-most tangential rays of the sun are striking the earth.

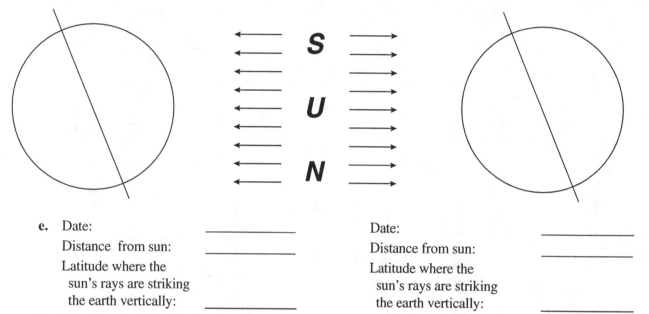

e.   Date: _____   Date: _____

Distance from sun: _____   Distance from sun: _____

Latitude where the   Latitude where the
  sun's rays are striking   sun's rays are striking
  the earth vertically: _____   the earth vertically: _____

f.   The diagrams below represent a new vantage point in space (180 degrees from the above diagrams). *Repeat* steps a through d for each of the following diagrams.

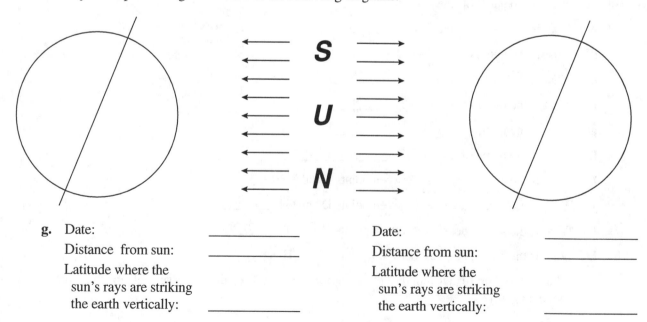

g.   Date: _____   Date: _____

Distance from sun: _____   Distance from sun: _____

Latitude where the   Latitude where the
  sun's rays are striking   sun's rays are striking
  the earth vertically: _____   the earth vertically: _____

name   section   date

3.3 The parallel arrows in the diagram below represent the rays of the sun on each given date. Each part of the diagram is a view of the earth's Northern Hemisphere (equal-area polar projection).

a. You are to draw the circle of illumination on each date. On three dates the exact location is required. On two of the dates a very close approximation is necessary.

b. Lightly shade in each nighttime area.

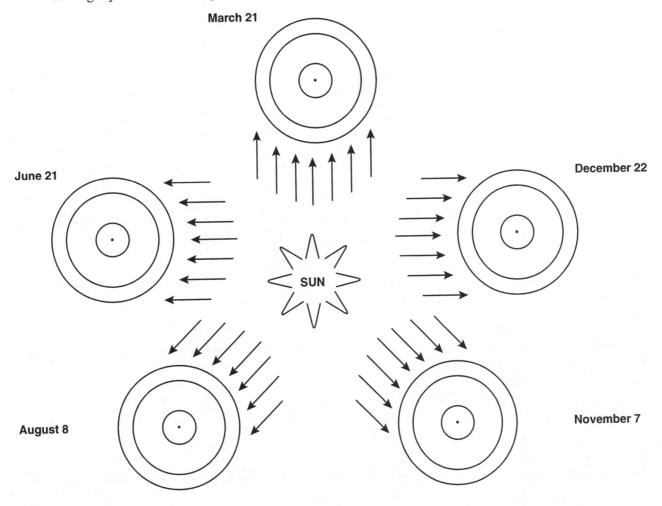

c. Do the same as in Exercises 3.3a and 3.3b for the one date given on the following diagram. Assume that the diagram is a view of the earth's *Southern* Hemisphere. (The sun is to the *left* of the diagram.).

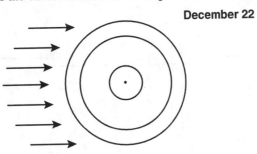

name   section   date

3.4 Calculate the *altitude angle* of the noon sun for each location and date given below. Show your calculations and put your final answer to each problem on the line in each computation box.

Latitude	March 21 and September 23	June 21	December 22
10° N			
25° N			
50° N			
80° N			
15° S			
62° S			

name   section   date

3.5 Calculate the *altitude* angle of the noon sun at 43 degrees N for March 21, June 21, September 23, and December 22 in the space below. Then plot these angles on the diagram to the right.

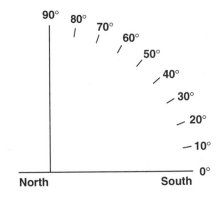

3.6 What is the *annual range* of *altitude angles* of the noon sun at

a. the poles? _____

b. the tropics? _____

c. the equator? _____

3.7 Calculate the *latitude* in each problem below. Show your calculations and put your final answer to each problem on the line in each computation box.

a. Altitude angle: 20° N horizon. Declination: 20° N. _____	**b.** Altitude angle: 60° S horizon. Declination: 15° N. _____
c. Altitude angle: 88° S horizon. Declination: 23° N. _____	**d.** Altitude angle: 75° N horizon. Declination: 18° S _____
e. Altitude angle: 87° S horizon. Declination: 1° S. _____	**f.** Altitude angle: 35° S horizon. Declination: 10° N. _____

name   section   date

Review and Study Questions

1. Explain why the energy from the sun decreases as the zenith angle increases.

2. Describe how the daylight period varies by latitude on June 21.

3. Explain how the daylight period varies throughout the year at (a) the equator and (b) the poles.

4. Explain *with diagrams* why there are six-month periods of daylight and darkness at the poles.

chapter 4

SOLAR RADIATION

Chapter 3, Earth–Sun Relationships, provides the basis for understanding the earth's receipt of solar radiation. How much energy might be received is largely determined by sun angles and the duration of the sunlight period. This chapter is concerned with calculating solar radiation values, depicting them graphically, and understanding the general nature and patterns of insolation. Chapter 5, Temperature, interrelates all these factors and shows how insolation patterns explain the basic temperature patterns.

Calculating Solar Radiation

The **solar constant** (*Jo*) can be used to calculate the amount of solar radiation (*J*) reaching a given area. The solar constant is the total solar radiation *outside* the atmosphere measured at normal incidence and assuming the mean earth–sun distance. Under these conditions the value of the solar constant is traditionally taken as 1.9408 langleys per minute (ly/min; 1 langley = 1 calorie per square centimeter).

If we disregard the atmosphere and wish to calculate the solar radiation received at a given latitude on a given date, we need to know the altitude angle of the sun at that latitude on that date. Chapter 3 explained how to determine the altitude angle for solar noon. This noontime angle will give the *maximum* solar radiation possible at noon on that date. This maximum noontime radiation (disregarding the atmosphere!) is calculated:

$$J = Jo \sin h$$

where *J* is solar radiation, *Jo* is the solar constant, and *h* is the altitude angle at solar noon. Sin *h* can be found from Table 3 in Appendix A.

Example:
Location: New Orleans (30 degrees N)
Date: December 22

(1)	30.0°	N	
	+23.5°	S	declination
	53.5°		arc
(2)	90.0°		
	−53.5°		
	36.5°		*h* (altitude angle)
(3)	.595		sin *h* (from Table 3)
	× 1.941		*Jo* (solar constant)
	1.155		*J* (solar radiation)

Drawing Insolation Curves

When drawing insolation curves (and other curves for data controlled by solar declination), remember that the change in declination is not uniform. Declination changes most rapidly during the month immediately before or after an equinox (11.75 degrees per month) and most slowly during the month immediately before or after a solstice (3.25 degrees per month). For the remaining months the declination rate is 8.5 degrees per month. This nonuniform rate of change is also true for the altitude angle of the sun during one day. The sun appears to rise rapidly during the hour after sunrise and set rapidly during the hour before sunset. The change in altitude angle, however, is much slower during the hours before and after solar noon.

This nonuniform rate of change means that annual insolation curves should be drawn with somewhat flattened highs and lows for the solstices. Diurnal curves should exhibit steepness near sunrise and sunset and some flatness near solar noon. Such curves should never have pointed peaks and valleys.

Interpolating Data

It is frequently necessary to interpolate between known values given in a simplified table. Such interpolation will be necessary when using Table 3, Trigonometric Functions, and Table 6, Length of the Daylight Period, in Appendix A (necessary for the exercises in this chapter). Several other situations will come up that will require interpolation of data. If a number is not listed in a table, but falls between two listed numbers, its value must be interpolated from between values for the two numbers that are given. In such a case, the data in the table should be examined to discern the trend, or rate of change in values, in the sequence of known intervals. Interpolation is sufficient if it applies this trend to the value between those given. Study the following example where the values do not change uniformly for every 5 degrees:

5° — 22 units
10° — 20 units
15° — 15 units
20° — 8 units

Notice that between 5 degrees and 10 degrees, each degree change of 1.0 implies an *average* unit change of 0.4. Between 10 degrees and 15 degrees, each degree change of 1.0 implies an *average* unit change of 1.0. Between 15 degrees and 20 degrees, each degree change of 1.0 implies an *average* unit change of 1.4. Because of this trend in the data we can interpolate that the value of 11 degrees must be a little more than 19 units while the value of 14 degrees must be a little less than 16 units.

If the interval used in a table is too broad for the degree of accuracy you require and you find it impossible to interpolate accurately with a moderate amount of effort, common sense suggests that you find a more detailed table elsewhere. They are available for just about everything.

name   section   date

Exercises

DRAWING INSOLATION CURVES

4.1 The procedure for calculating maximum possible noontime solar radiation ($J = Jo \sin h$) is demonstrated in the example on page 28. Remember that the procedure for calculating the altitude angle at solar noon (h) is given in Chapter 3. The sine of this angle ($\sin h$) may be found in Table 3 in Appendix A.

Using the formula ($J = Jo \sin h$), calculate the maximum possible noontime solar radiation, for each solstice and equinox, for each of the following cities.

a. Haverhill, Massachusetts (43.0 degrees N)
b. Canton, China (23.5 degrees N)
c. Entebbe, Uganda (on the equator)

Show your calculations in the space below. Then *plot* these maxima on the graph below and draw smooth curves, clearly labeled, for each location.

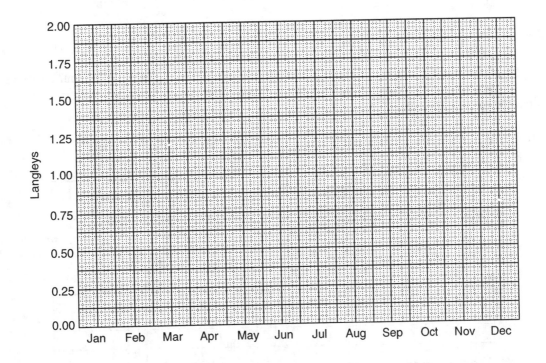

name   section   date

4.2   Using Table 6, Length of the Daylight Period (in Appendix A), and the noontime maxima values for Haverhill, Massachusetts calculated in the previous problem, plot diurnal insolation curves for Haverhill. The graph below should have three curves, clearly labeled: one curve for both equinoxes and one curve for each of the solstices.

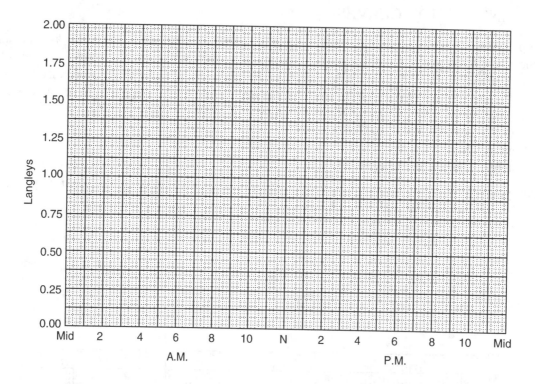

4.3   On the graph below, draw curves representing the *annual insolation* regimes for the four locations given below. No *calculations* are required. These curves are to be correct in a relative sense (their positions should be correct *relative* to each other).

Locations: **a.** 0 degrees   **b.** 30 degrees N   **c.** 60 degrees N   **d.** 90 degrees N

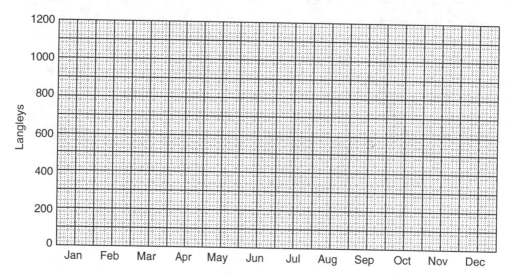

name section date

4.4 On the graph below, draw curves representing the *diurnal* insolation regimes for *June 21* for the four locations given below. Again, no calculations are necessary. The curves are to be correct in a relative sense. You will need to use Table 6, Length of the Daylight Period (in Appendix A).

Locations: **a.** 0 degrees **b.** 30 degrees N **c.** 60 degrees N **d.** 90 degrees N

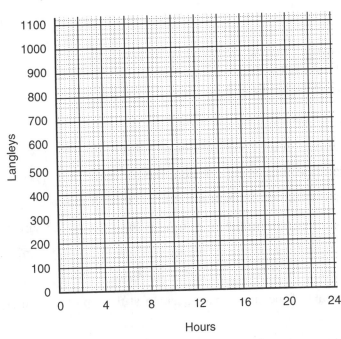

4.5 On the following graph, draw (and clearly label) curves representing the *annual* insolation regimes for the locations given.

Locations: **a.** 50.0 degrees N **b.** 50.0 degrees S **c.** 66.5 degrees S **d.** 80.0 degrees S

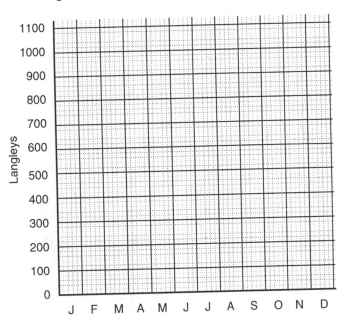

name   section   date

RADIATION BUDGET

4.6 The following list shows some significant parts of the global radiation budget. The values are *mean* values, as percentages of the total radiation (100%) at the outside boundary of the earth's atmosphere. The percentages and estimated values in kilolangleys per year (in parentheses) are given

Reflection from clouds to space	20%	(53)
Absorbed by clouds	4	(11)
Diffuse reflection to space by dust and Rayleigh scattering	6	(16)
Absorbed by air molecules (CO_2, O_3, H_2O) and dust	15	(40)
Reflection to space from the earth's surface	4	(11)

Using these data, answer the following questions.

a. What is the total percentage of incoming radiation reflected by the atmosphere? _____

b. What is the total percentage of incoming radiation absorbed by the atmosphere? _____

c. What percentage of incoming radiation is transmitted to the earth's surface? _____

d. What percentage of incoming radiation is actually absorbed by the earth's surface? _____

e. What percentage is lost to space in reflection by the earth–atmosphere system? _____

f. What is the total percentage absorbed by the earth–atmosphere system? _____

g. What is the total amount of incoming solar radiation at the top of the atmosphere in kilolangleys per year? _____

h. Describe the factors that greatly *increase* or *decrease* the actual amount of solar radiation (insolation) reaching the earth's surface, in comparison to the above mean value.

name section date

ROOF OVERHANG AND SOLAR ENERGY

4.7 The diagram below is of a south-facing wall of a house located at 45 degrees N. Determine the proper length for the roof overhang to maximize incoming solar radiation in the winter and minimize the radiation at the window in the summer.

a. In the space below, to the left of the house, calculate the maximum sun angles (at noon) for June 21 and December 22.

b. Using a protractor, plot these angles to show two pairs of parallel lines, one pair for each season, intersecting the plane of the window. One pair of parallel lines represents the sun's rays in summer and the other pair represents the rays in winter. Each pair should be drawn at the correct angle and be properly labeled. Each pair should be of a width that represents only the rays that could enter the window.

c. Draw solid lines to *extend* the roof overhang so as to allow maximum winter radiation to enter the window but to minimize the summer radiation as well.

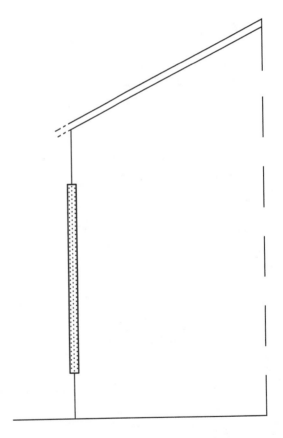

d. What new building regulations (regarding street layout, house alignment, etc.) does the above suggest, with regard to developments of numerous new homes on large tracts of undeveloped land?

name   section   date

Review and Study Questions

1.   What are the three processes of transmission of heat energy? Define each term.

2.   What is meant by a radiation surplus and a radiation deficit? Where does the *balance* of radiation received and lost occur?

3.   Describe the solar spectrum.

4.   Which wavelengths provide most of the energy at the earth's surface?

5.   What is the solar constant? What is its quantitative value?

6.   When solar radiation enters the earth's atmosphere, one of three things can happen to it. These three possibilities are:

7.   Define the term *albedo*. What determines the albedo of a surface?

8.   The atmosphere is heated by the earth's radiation in what wavelength?

9.   Define the term *insolation*.

10.   *Define* the principle of *land and water contrasts* (sometimes called the law of land and water differences).

11.   *Explain* each of the four main factors that cause land and water to respond differently to equal amounts of insolation. (That is, explain the principle of land and water contrasts.)

12.   *Define* the **greenhouse effect** of the atmosphere. (The next question asks for the causes!)

13.   *Explain* what causes the greenhouse effect of the atmosphere.

14. *Explain* the process of **radiation cooling** and describe its effects.

15. Why does the South Pole receive more solar radiation in December than the North Pole does in June?

16. The amount of insolation at the earth's surface is not uniform. Insolation varies by latitude at any given moment. It also varies through time at any given latitude. *List* and briefly explain each of the four or five major factors that account for this variation or irregularity in insolation.

17. Even if two places in the same latitude *received* the same amount of solar radiation on the same day, these two places could vary greatly in the amount of radiation they *absorb*. What are the two major factors that could cause these differences in absorption?

chapter **5**

TEMPERATURE

The relationship of solar radiation to heat energy and, consequently, temperature is basic and substantial. Chapters 3 and 4 of this manual outline earth–sun relationships and the nature of solar radiation. After having worked through these chapters, you should understand the reasons for variations in the amount of solar radiation by latitude and by time of day and time of year, as well as the factors that influence the absorptivity of this radiation by the earth's surface and atmosphere. These topics should be reviewed with special attention to the cyclic rhythm of incoming solar radiation, the greenhouse effect of the atmosphere, the principles of continental–maritime contrasts, albedos, and the role of atmospheric conditions.

The role of temperature (or heat) in explaining atmospheric processes and its relationship to other weather elements are treated in subsequent chapters.

There are numerous such relationships. For example, air temperatures are related to the global pressure field and, consequently, to the general circulation of the atmosphere and planetary winds. Temperature conditions help to explain some local winds, and combinations of wind and temperature are important to the ways in which people sense heat or cold (as is demonstrated by the wind-chill factor). Heat and air temperature are essential factors in all the moisture processes from evaporation and relative humidity to condensation and, ultimately, precipitation.

The atmosphere, together with the oceans, behaves as a huge heat engine driven by energy from the sun and the earth's gravitational forces. This broad picture of the role of heat energy, expressed as temperature, should be kept in mind while doing the following exercises.

GRAPH A:

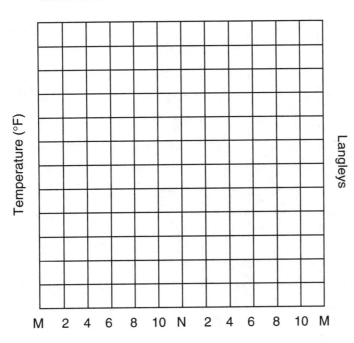

GRAPH B:

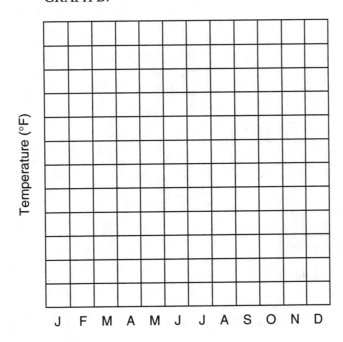

GRAPH C:

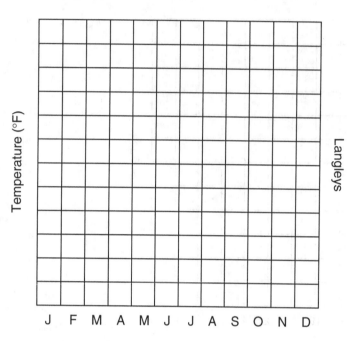

GRAPH D:

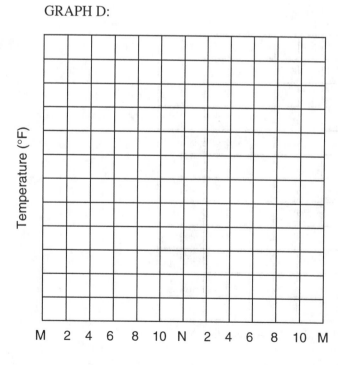

name   section   date

OBSERVED TEMPERATURE ISOTHERMS

5.5 **a.** The following map shows the actual temperatures observed at 7:00 A.M. on a day in mid-November. Show the temperature pattern by drawing the *isotherms*, using a ten-degree interval, and labeling all isotherms.

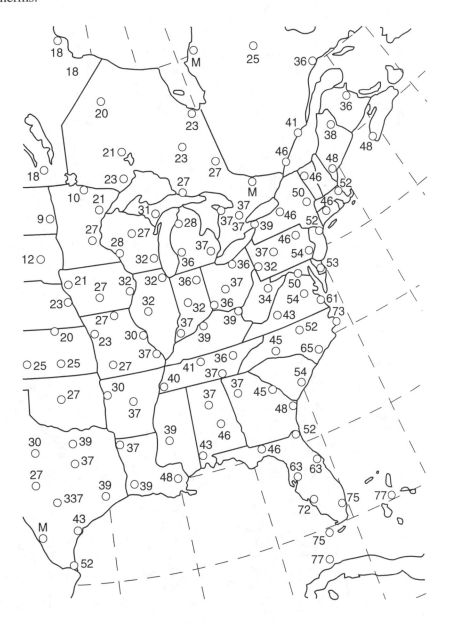

b. Which single isotherm (either drawn on the above map or *implied* between two that are drawn) is considered highly significant—and why?

name   section   date

MAXIMUM AND MINIMUM ISOTHERMS

5.6 The *maximum* temperatures for the day and the *minimum* temperatures for the day are given on the maps below. These data are for the *same day* in mid-November as that used in Exercise 5.5. The maximum and minimum temperatures are those that occured at any moment during the 24-hr. period of that day. Draw the isotherms on each map, using a ten-degree interval, to show the respective isothermal patterns of maximum and minimum temperatures on that day.

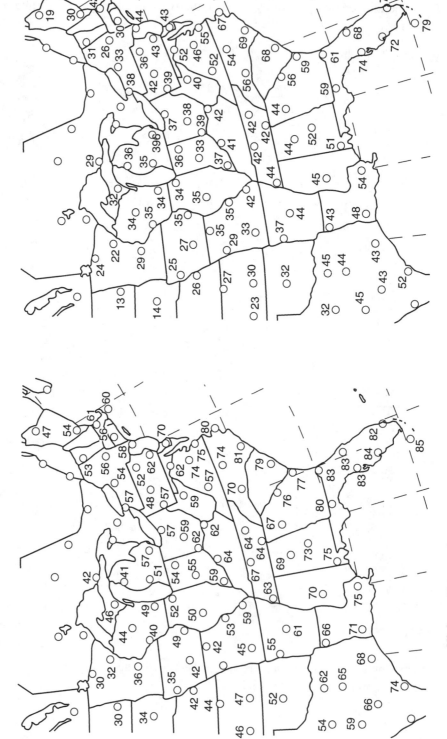

Minimum Temperatures

Minimum Temperatures

name   section   date

DIURNAL TEMPERATURE RANGE ISOTHERMS

5.7   **a.**   In the previous exercises you have shown the isothermal patterns of observed temperatures, maximum temperatures, and minimum temperatures. If, for each individual station, the maximum and minimum temperatures are taken and *averaged*, these means can be plotted on a map and isotherms can be drawn to show the pattern of average temperatures for that day.

Now you are asked to examine the *diurnal range* of temperatures for this same mid-November day. Subtract the minimum temperature from the maximum temperature for each individual station and plot this diurnal range on the map below. Next, draw isotherms for the values of a 10-degree range and a 25-degree range. Finally, lightly shade in those areas that had a diurnal temperature range of 10 degrees or less, and sketch lines within those areas that had a diurnal temperature range of 25 degrees or more. (Different colors may be used instead of the shading and lines.)

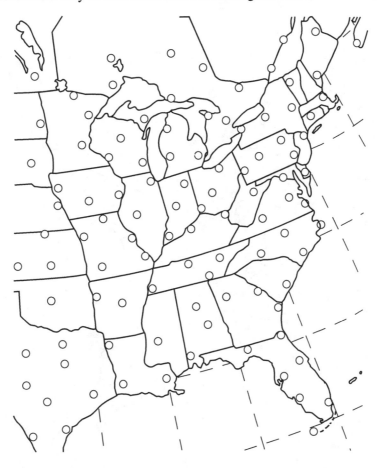

b.   What do you find *most unusual* about the diurnal temperature range pattern shown above?

name   section   date

THE DEGREE-DAY

5.8   The degree-day is useful to fuel suppliers in determining energy demand. During the cold season, the mean daily temperature is subtracted from 65°F to give the number of **heating degree-days**. During the warm season, the 65-degree base value is subtracted from the mean daily temperature to give the number of **cooling degree-days**. Estimates of degree-days, based upon forecasts of temperature, have become a basis for anticipating fuel requirements for winter heating and summer cooling loads. Comparisons of current cumulative degree-days with mean values from past records provide early insights into supply problems.

Using the data from Exercise 5.7 (maximum and minimum temperatures for a mid-November day), compute the heating degree-days and cooling degree-days for each station. Plot these numbers on the map below (with a plus sign for heating degree-days and a minus sign for cooling degree-days). Then draw the degree-day isopleths for +30, +20, + 10, 0, and –10.

name   section   date

VERTICAL TEMPERATURE PROFILES AND THE OBSERVED LAPSE RATE

5.9   The following temperatures were obtained by radiosonde at 4:00 P.M. on three different days. Temperatures are in degrees Fahrenheit and altitude is in thousands of feet.

	Altitude										
	0	**1**	**2**	**3**	**4**	**5**	**6**	**7**	**8**	**9**	**10**
April 8	52	48	45	41	38	34	30	27	23	20	17
June 9	60	57	54	56	58	54	50	47	43	39	35
December 10	40	43	45	41	38	34	30	27	23	20	17

Plot these data on the following graphs and draw curves to show the vertical temperature profiles.

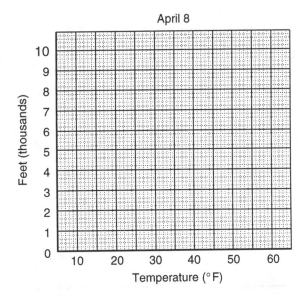

April 8

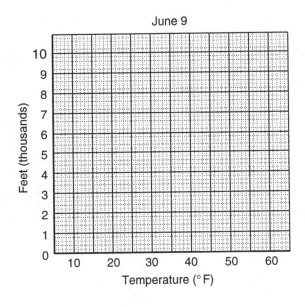

June 9

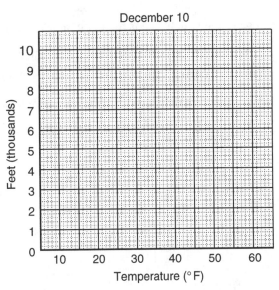

December 10

5.10 The observed (actual) temperature lapse rate is the rate of temperature change per unit of vertical (altitudinal) distance. It assumes static or stationary air (no vertical motion or air currents). Temperatures are obtained from various altitudes, and the lapse rate is found by dividing the vertical distance between two temperature observations into the difference in temperatures between the two altitudes involved. In Fahrenheit, the rate is expressed per 1000 ft. In Celsius, it is expressed per 100 m or per km. Whenever warmer air is found above colder air, a **temperature inversion** exists, the lapse rate is positive for that region of the atmosphere, and the air is usually stable.

Using the radiosonde data in Exercise 5.9, calculate the observed lapse rates in the boxes below and put your answers on the lines in each box.

a. April 8: 0–10,000 ft	**d.** April 8: 4000–10,000 ft
b. June 9: 0–10,000 ft	**e.** June 9: 4000–10,000 ft
c. December 10: 0–10,000 ft	**f.** December 10: 4000–10,000 ft

g. On which date is the lapse rate "normal"? _____

h. On which date is there a *surface* inversion? _____

i. On which date is there an *upper-air* inversion? _____

j. Which date has the highest *positive* lapse rate? _____

k. What is the highest positive lapse rate? _____

name   section   date

Review and Study Questions

1.   What are the primary *processes* by which heat energy is added to the lower atmosphere?

2.   Are the processes for losing heat by the atmosphere different, and if so, in what ways?

3.   What is a temperature inversion?

4.   What is the numerical value of the *normal* temperature lapse rate?

5.   What is the difference between the *normal* temperature lapse rate and an *observed* temperature lapse rate?

6.   Explain the concept of *temperature time lag*.

7.   What is the difference between heat and temperature?

8.   Explain the differences in construction of a maximum thermometer and a minimum thermometer including the fluids used.

9. Explain the advantages and disadvantages of the thermograph as well as the advantages and disadvantages of the differences in the time divisions on the graphs of various thermographs.

10. What are the major requirements for the proper placement of a thermometer?

11. Using the isothermal maps of the world (found in most textbooks and atlases), answer the following questions:

    a. Where (specifically) is the hottest area in the world in the *summer* season?

    b. Name the location of *four* other summer-season hot regions.

    c. What location (other than Antarctica) has the lowest *winter* temperature average?

    d. Where are the lowest *annual* average temperatures found?

    e. What specific location has the greatest *annual range* of temperature?

    f. How much of an annual range is found there?

    g. Where is the smallest *annual range* of temperature found?

    h. What is the overall directional trend of the isotherms—and why?

    i. Choose a *January* isotherm (such as 30°F) in the Northern Hemisphere and follow its path. Notice that it bends toward the equator when crossing a continent and bends poleward when approaching an ocean. Now choose a *July* isotherm (such as 60°F) in the Northern Hemisphere. Notice that it bends toward the pole as it moves into a continent and bends toward the equator as it approaches an ocean. Explain the reasons for this change in direction of isotherms in January and for its reversal in July.

    j. Why does the Southern Hemisphere show so much less bending of isotherms than d   ne Northern Hemisphere?

12. What is the effect of *vertical* air motion (both rising *and* descending) on the temperature of air?

13. Explain each of the major *causes* of vertical air motion.

14. Discuss as many different factors as you can that might explain the temperature conditions of a given location at a given moment in time (assuming the actual conditions are either normal, above normal, or below normal).

chapter 6

AIR PRESSURE

Atmospheric pressure is an *element* of weather and climate as well as a *control* or determinant of weather and climate. To our senses, it is the least discernible element of our weather. Air pressure is, however, highly correlated with actual conditions. High pressure is frequently associated with stability, clear skies (lots of sunshine), and dryness. Low pressure is usually associated with instability, cloudiness, higher humidity, and much precipitation. Most storms are, in fact, types of low pressure systems.

Although the absolute value of air pressure is useful information and may explain many conditions, the *changes* in air pressure are of much greater value for predicting both imminent and longer-term weather changes. The rate of change in pressure, the amount of the change, and the direction of the change are basic and invaluable pieces of weather information. A simple home barometer will provide this data.

Differences in pressure on the earth's surface are what causes air to move, under the influence of gravity, according to the pressure gradient. Wind is the result. Because wind is a major vehicle for the transportation of both heat energy and atmospheric moisture from one region to another, air-pressure patterns become an underlying factor in the explanation of both momentary and annual average weather and climatic conditions.

You should review the vertical profile of pressure in the atmosphere presented in Exercise 2.3. The relationship between pressure and wind is further explored in Chapter 7, Wind and the Global Circulation. The major topics that have been presented thus far, such as earth–sun relationships, solar radiation, temperature, and pressure, are all interrelated. Because a pressure pattern may have been thermally induced, the explanation of that pressure pattern may be traced back to the temperature pattern, the distribution of solar radiation that caused the temperature pattern, and ultimately to the earth's physical relationship to the sun at that time, which explains the radiation distribution.

Average Values

It is useful to know the *average* value for sea-level air pressure (also known as one *standard atmosphere*) and to have an idea of the typical range in sea-level pressure. Average sea-level air pressure, in different units, is as follows:

1013.25	millibars (mb)
29.92	inches of mercury (in. Hg)
760	millimeters of mercury (mm Hg)
14.7	pounds per square inch (lb/in^2)
2116.8	pounds per square foot (lb/ft^2)
101,325	newtons per square meter (N/m^2) (also called a pascal)
101.33	kilopascals (kPa)

See Tables 1 and 2 in Appendix A for additional special SI pressure terms and conversion factors. Since the millibar and inches of mercury are most frequently encountered in meteorology, some useful conversion factors are:

1 mb	=	0.02953 in. Hg
1 in. Hg	=	33.8639 mb
1 in. Hg	=	25.4 mm Hg

Sea-level air pressure is seldom "normal" or average. It is usually higher or lower than the average.

1050 mb (31 in. Hg) is very high pressure while 980 mb (28.94 in. Hg) is very low pressure. These values provide a range for highs and lows of 70 mb (2.1 in. Hg). However, record extremes have occurred that include unusual winter highs, such as 1084 mb (32.01 in. Hg) in Siberia (Dec. 1968) and 1064 mb (31.42 in. Hg) in Montana (Dec. 1983). Record low pressures, usually associated with the eyes of hurricanes, include many readings in the 950–900 mb range. A record low of 870 mb (25.69 in. Hg) occurred in the Pacific Ocean in the eye of Typhoon Tip (Oct. 1979).

Upper-air Pressure

The above data are *sea-level* values. Chapter 2 introduced the normal vertical profile of pressure from sea-level upward through the atmosphere (also see Table 7 in Appendix A). Variations in high and low pressure areas *within* the atmosphere are also extremely important and are recognized from *upper-air* maps. An upper-air pressure surface is a *constant pressure* surface where the *altitude* of that constant pressure varies. Thus, the *heights* of a constant pressure value are shown using height contours in feet or in decameters (tens-of-meters). For a given pressure value, low altitudes mean low pressure there while higher altitudes mean higher pressure there (at the *same* constant pressure surface). Think of it this way: normally, the 500 mb pressure surface is found at 18,000 feet (see Table 8 in Appendix A). If, *overhead* today, you find that a pressure of 500 mb is reached at an altitude of only 16,000 feet, then you would have *low* pressure overhead at the 500 mb level. Because the pressure is 500 mb at 16,000 feet, it must be even

lower if you go higher up to the standard height of 18,000 feet to reach the standard 500 mb surface.

Coding and Decoding

For each weather station shown on the surface weather map, air pressure is given as a three-digit number in millibars. This three-digit number includes one decimal place, but the decimal point is omitted. The three-digit number *also omits* the *first* or the *first two* digits of the actual air pressure value. A pressure of 989.3 mb would be shown on the map as 893 (first digit and decimal point omitted). A pressure of 1018.7 mb would be coded as 187 (first *two* digits and the decimal point omitted). Decoding (or reading) these three-digit pressures from the map reverses this process. A value coded as 964 would be decoded and read as 996.4 mb (decimal point added and the missing digit 9 added). A coded value of 075 would be decoded and read as 1007.5 mb (decimal point and missing *two* digits added back). Deciding whether a 9 or a 10 has been dropped is a matter of experience and familiarity with the data and knowing what the general pressure situation in an area is or has been. However, a useful rule of thumb is this: If the first number of the coded three digits is *higher than 5*, a 9 is missing; if the first number is a 5 *or lower*, a 10 is missing. This rule of thumb works for pressures between 960.0 mb and 1049.9 mb, a range which includes about 99% of all observed pressures. Extreme pressures above or below these limits are seldom experienced. When they are, the situation should be obvious: An exceptional low pressure cell has been developing or a very extraordinary high pressure cell has been forming, most likely over a period of several days.

name   section   date

Exercises

MEASURES OF AIR PRESSURE

Using the information from the preceding text, complete Exercises 6.1 through 6.4.

6.1 Fill in the values for average sea-level air pressure (one **standard atmosphere**) in the following list.

    _____ millibars
    _____ inches of mercury
    _____ millimeters of mercury
    _____ pounds per square inch
    _____ pounds per square foot

6.2 Fill in the *typical* values for low, normal, and high sea-level air pressures.

	Low	Normal	High
Millibars:	_____	_____	_____
Inches of mercury:	_____	_____	_____

6.3 From Table 8 in Appendix A, what is the height above sea level, in feet and in meters, for the following **standard pressure surfaces** used on upper-air charts.

Standard surface	Feet	Meters
850-mb surface	_____	_____
700-mb surface	_____	_____
500-mb surface	_____	_____
400-mb surface	_____	_____
200-mb surface	_____	_____

6.4 What is an upper-air standard pressure surface?

6.5 a. If, *directly above you*, a pressure of 500 mb is found at a height of 23,500 feet, then describe the pressure at the 500 mb surface.

b. If, *directly above you*, a pressure of 500 mb is found at a height of 15,000 feet, then describe the pressure at the 500 mb surface.

name   section   date

CODING AND DECODING PRESSURE DATA

6.6   Using the information in the Coding and Decoding section of the preceding text, write the three-digit coded form for each pressure value given in the "decoded pressure" column. Then write the decoded form for each coded pressure given in the next column.

Decoded pressure	Coded	Coded pressure	Decoded
a. 1051.1 mb	_____	j. 095	_____
b. 1037.5 mb	_____	k. 127	_____
c. 1018.6 mb	_____	l. 253	_____
d. 1009.0 mb	_____	m. 920	_____
e. 1003.8 mb	_____	n. 838	_____
f. 1000.0 mb	_____	o. 337	_____
g. 996.6 mb	_____	p. 981	_____
h. 973.4 mb	_____	q. 786	_____
i. 958.1 mb	_____	r. 907	_____

s.   Which of the above values do not fit the rule of thumb for decoding?

PRESSURE CONVERSIONS

6.7   Perform the following air pressure conversions using the conversion factors given in the preceding text.

a. 1000 mb   =   _____ in. Hg

b. 500 mb   =   _____ in. Hg

c. 30 in. Hg   =   _____ mb

d. 30 in. Hg   =   _____ mm Hg

e. There is _____ pounds of force on an 8½"× 11" piece of paper.

f. There is _____ pounds of force on a 10 ft^2 surface area.

name   section   date

DRAWING ISOBARS AND THE PRESSURE FIELD

6.8   Map 6.1 presents a highly simplified pressure field. Draw all the necessary isobars, using a 4-mb interval and using the 1000-mb isobar as a basis. This means that all isobars must be multiples of 4 mb for values above and below the 1000-mb isobar. How many isobars must be drawn always depends on the actual data. You may wish to review the section on The Nature of Isopleths and Drawing Isopleths in Chapter 1 before you begin.

It is usually easier, while learning, if you first decode the pressure values. On the map, add the missing decimal point (for tenths) and add the missing 9 or 10 in front of the three-digit number. The pressures will be much less confusing and the pressure field much clearer to see.

Remember: Isopleths (in this case, isobars) should be drawn *lightly in pencil* until all necessary isopleths have been drawn, checked, and adjusted. Also, every isobar should be *labeled* and the labels should be kept in the same general vicinity on the map, if possible.

name   section   date

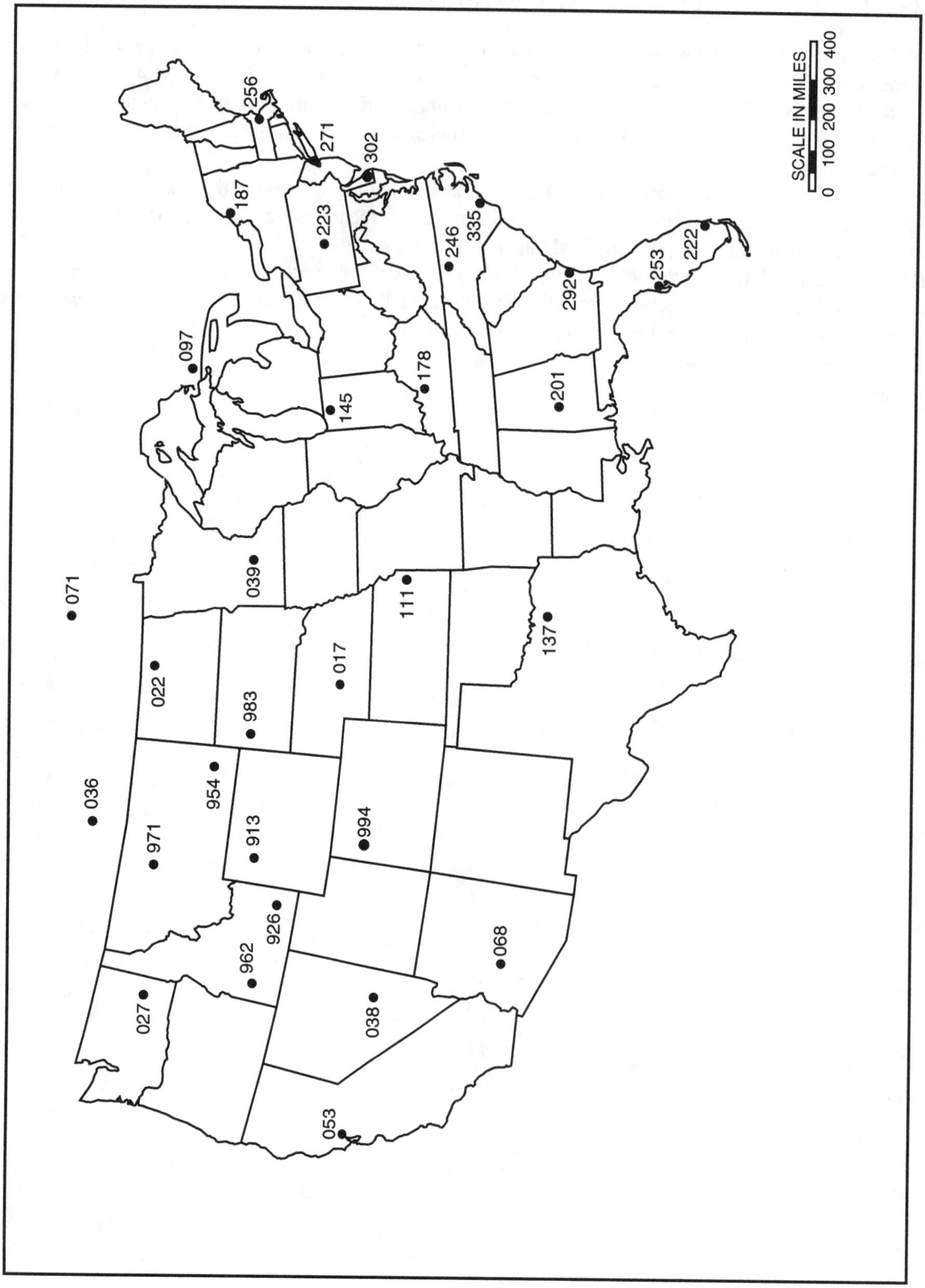

Map 6.1 (For use in Exercise 6.8)

SCALE IN MILES
0 100 200 300 400

256
271
302
187
223
246
335
292
253
222
097
145
178
201
071
039
111
022
983
017
137
036
954
971
913
994
962
926
027
068
038
053

name   section   date

PRESSURE GRADIENTS

6.9   The **pressure gradient** is the change in pressure per unit of horizontal distance. It is found by dividing the distance between two places *into* the difference in pressure between those two places. If the distance is in miles, the answer is per mile. If the distance is *first* divided by 100 (*or* the answer is multiplied by 100 *afterward*—the answer is then given per 100 mi instead of per mile. Such gradients are *average* gradients for the unit distances.

From the information below, calculate the *pressure gradient per 100 mi* between each pair of cities and for the total distance between Wichita and Baltimore. Do your calculations in the boxes below and place your answers on the lines provided.

City	Pressure	Distance between cities
Wichita	1025 mb	.... 450 mi
St. Louis	1022 mb	.... 340 mi
Cincinnati	1011 mb	.... 500 mi
Baltimore	1004 mb	

a. Wichita to St. Louis:

_____

b. St. Louis to Cincinnati:

_____

a. Cincinnati to Baltimore:

_____

b. Wichita to Baltimore:

_____

name   section   date

PRESSURE TENDENCY AND NET CHANGE

6.10 The **pressure tendency** symbols on the weather map indicate the nature of any changes of pressure during the three-hour period preceding the hour of observation. Pressure tendency gives the trend of the readings on a barometer—such as rising, falling, steady, rising then falling, and falling then rising. The **net change** is the amount of pressure change during the three-hour period preceding the hour of observation. It is always given in tenths of millibars with the decimal omitted (+5 means 0.5 mb higher than three hours ago and –21 means 2.1 mb lower than three hours ago). Applying the net change to the current pressure reading will give the air pressure three hours earlier.

Using the daily weather map for November 10 (Map 6.2) give the data called for in each column for each location.

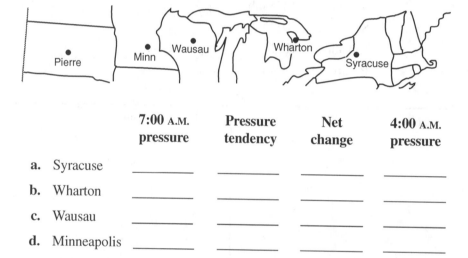

		7:00 A.M. **pressure**	**Pressure** **tendency**	**Net** **change**	**4:00 A.M.** **pressure**
a.	Syracuse	_____	_____	_____	_____
b.	Wharton	_____	_____	_____	_____
c.	Wausau	_____	_____	_____	_____
d.	Minneapolis	_____	_____	_____	_____
e.	Pierre	_____	_____	_____	_____

f. What pattern can you find in the changing pressure tendencies from Syracuse to Pierre as the storm center moves from southwest to northeast?

g. How many *distinct* cells of low pressure (cyclones) are on the map?

h. How many *regions* of low pressure are on the map?

i. What is the *highest* pressure found on the map?

name   section   date

DETERMINING STORM TRACKS AND SPEED

6.11 The center of a pressure cell marks its position at that time. On the daily weather map, the locations of well-defined pressure centers are also given for intervals of 6, 12, and 18 hr preceding the map time by the symbol: **X**. Chains of arrows between these symbols indicate the tracks of such pressure systems. For the following exercise, use the daily weather maps of November 10 and November 11 (Maps 6.2 and 6.3). You will also need Map 6.4 (a blank weather map) for plotting purposes. All parts of this exercise go on the *same* map. Take your time and plot the information accurately. Plot lightly at first so that corrections and adjustments may be made on the same map.

   a. On Map 6.4 plot the position of each of the two major low-pressure centers from Map 6.2 (November 10). Label the day and hour, next to the plotted position, as 11/10—7 A.M. (for November 10 at 7:00 A.M.).

   b. On the same plotting map, plot the position of *each* of the two lows for the 6, 12, and 18 hr preceding the 7:00 A.M. positions. Carefully label each position by date and hour.

   c. On the same plotting map, *repeat* the process using information from Map 6.3 (November 11). First, plot the position of each low at 7:00 A.M. Then plot the positions of each of the two lows for the 6, 12, and 18 hr preceding 7:00 A.M., November 11. Be sure to plot these positions accurately and to label each position by date and hour. Your map should now show the positions of each of the two low pressure centers for a 42-hr period.

   d. Show the separate 42-hr storm tracks of each low by connecting the positions of each storm with arrows.

name   section   date

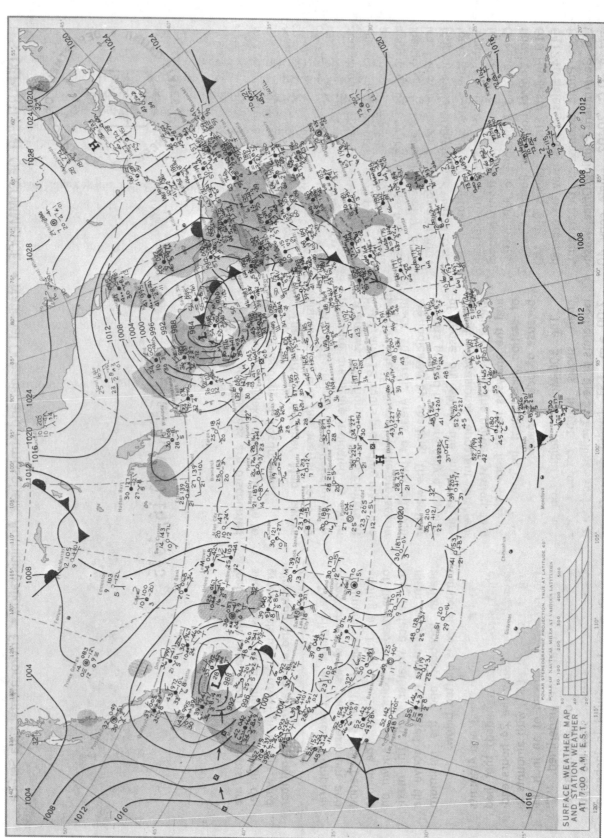

Map 6.2   Monday, November 10.

name   section   date

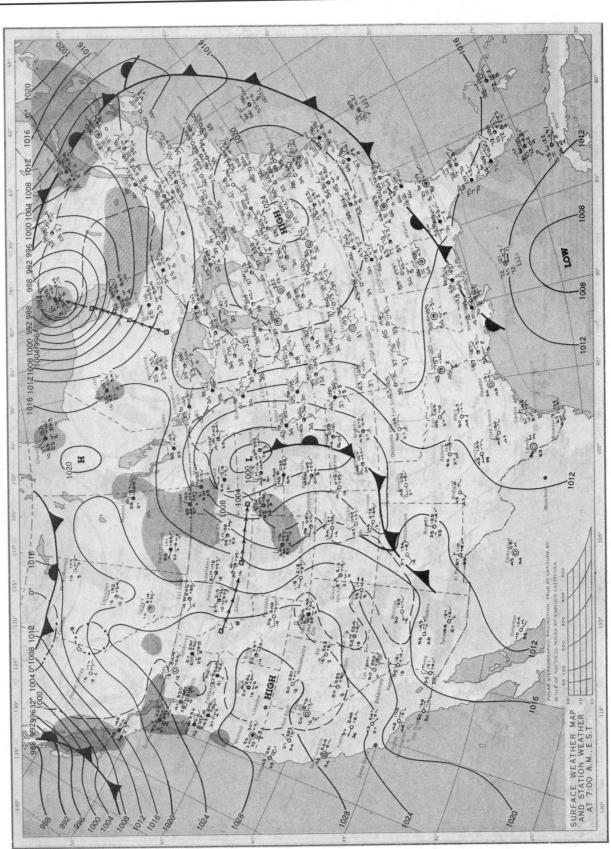

SURFACE WEATHER MAP
AND STATION WEATHER
AT 7:00 A.M. E.S.T.

Map 6.3   **Tuesday, November 11.**

name   section   date

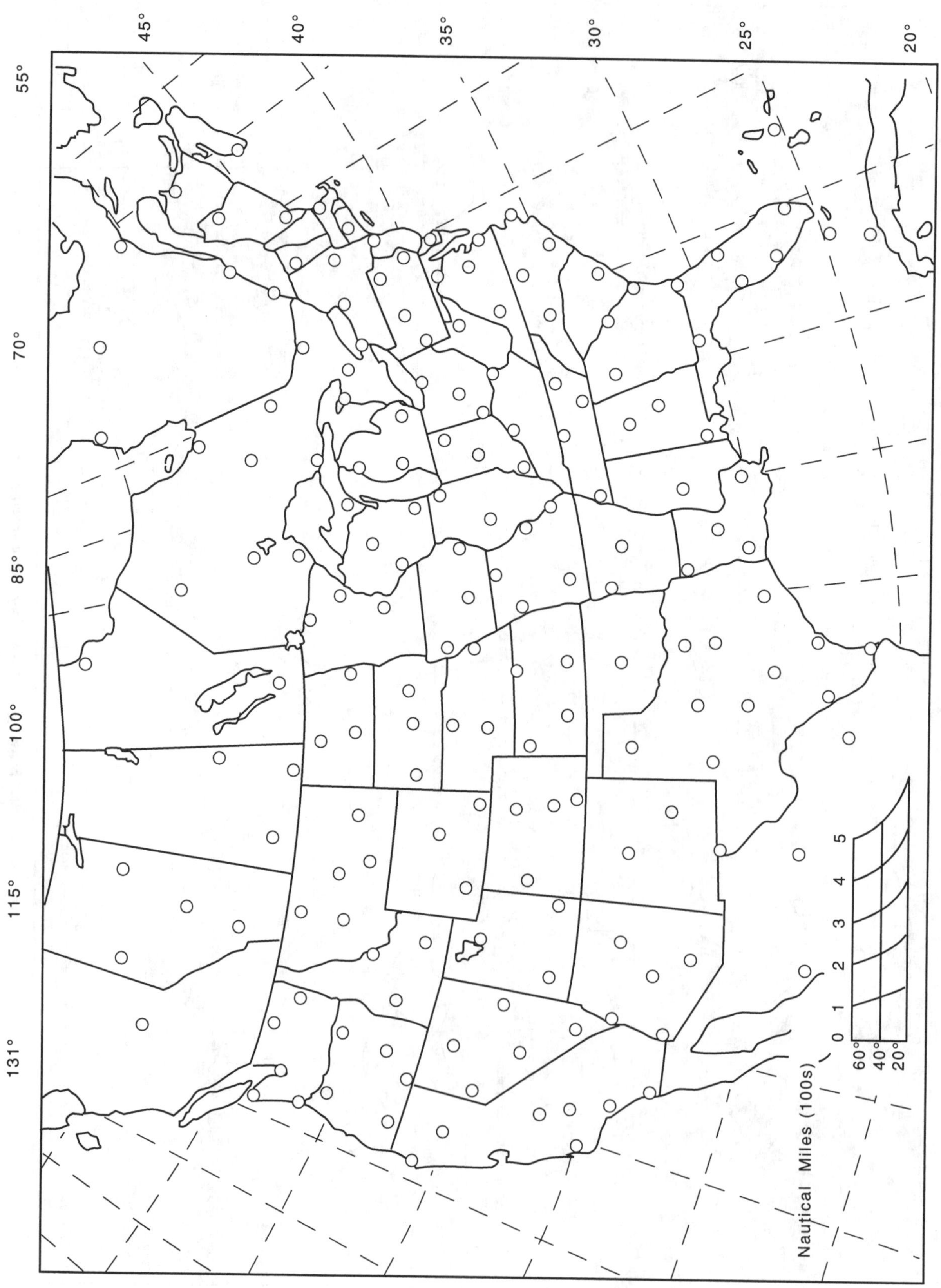

Map 6.4 (For use in Exercise 6.11)

name   section   date

RATE OF MOVEMENT OF PRESSURE SYSTEMS

6.12 To determine the *rate of movement* of a pressure center, divide the distance traveled by the time period involved. Thus, if a low-pressure cell has traveled 240 mi in 12 hr. it has averaged 20 MPH. You must follow the *track* of the pressure system, *not* the straight-line path between two distant positions. Use the edge of a piece of paper to mark the distance between positions on the map and then measure these distance marks made on the paper against the distance scale found on the map. It is very helpful to have the distance marks along the edge of the paper labeled carefully by date and hour.

Using *your* map of the two storm tracks prepared for Exercise 6.11 answer the following questions. Show all calculations in the spaces provided, and put such answers, properly labeled, on the lines.

a. What is the average speed of the West Coast low from its position in the Pacific Ocean at 1:00 P.M. on November 9 to its position in South Dakota at 7:00 A.M. on November 11?

_____

b. What is the average speed of the interior low that moved from southern Kansas at 1:00 P.M. on November 9 to its position near Hudson Bay at 7:00 A.M. on November 11?

_____

c. What was the speed of the West Coast low from 1:00 P.M. on November 9 to 7:00 A.M. on November 10?

_____

d. What was the speed of the West Coast low from 7:00 A.M. on November 10 to 7:00 A.M. on November 11?

_____

e. Did this West Coast storm speed up or slow down during this 42-hr period?

_____

f.   What was the speed of the interior (Kansas–Hudson Bay) storm from 1:00 P.M. on November 9 to 7:00 A.M. on November 10?

_____

g.   What was the speed of the interior low from 7:00 A.M. on November 10 to 7:00 A.M. on November 11?

_____

h.   Did this interior storm speed up or slow down during this 42-hr period?

_____

i.   How did the pressure in the *center* of each low change during the last 24 hr? What do you think this change means?

j.   A *high*-pressure cell was centered in Oklahoma at 7:00 A.M. on November 10. By 7:00 A.M. on November 11 it had moved to southwest Pennsylvania. Measure the distance this cell (an anticyclone) traveled and calculate its average speed of movement for this 24-hr period.

_____

k.   Compare the speed of the anticyclone with the speed of each of the two cyclones for the same 24-hr period. What tentative conclusions can you make?

name   section   date

GENERALIZED PRESSURE FIELDS

6.13 In the boxes below, sketch the general pattern of *isobars* that will depict each of the four types of pressure fields that are asked for. These will be generalized patterns with enough isobars to show each type of pressure field clearly. Label *at least two* isobars in each example, but do not bother to label every isobar. Do label the centers of the pressure fields either *high* or *low*.

a. An *anticyclone*, with the steepest gradient in the northeast sector.

b. A *cyclone*, with the steepest gradient in the western sector.

c. A *high pressure ridge* extending northwest to southeast with the steepest gradient on the southwest slope.

d. A *trough of low pressure* extending precisely east to west with *no* isobars shown as closed loops.

name   section   date

GLOBAL PRESSURE PATTERNS

6.14 Nearly every meteorology textbook has maps that show the January and July isobaric patterns of mean global pressure (usually combined with surface winds). Using the information from such isobaric maps, show the January and July pressure curves for the parallels and meridian given below. Use different colors or line symbols for different curves drawn on the same graph. Always label each curve clearly.

    a. Plot and then draw the curves for:

        1. January pressures, by latitude, for 80 degrees E longitude.

        2. July pressures, by latitude, for 80 degrees E longitude.

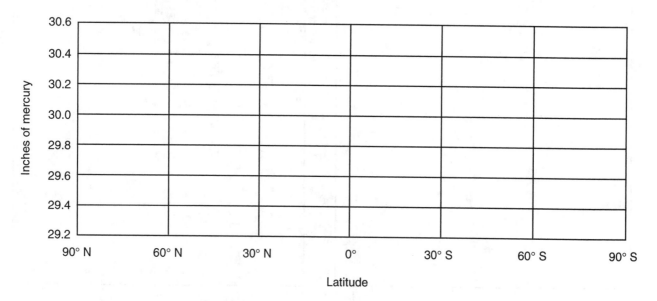

    b. Plot and then draw the curves for:

        1. January pressures, by longitude, for 50 degrees N latitude.

        2. July pressures, by longitude, for 30 degrees N latitude.

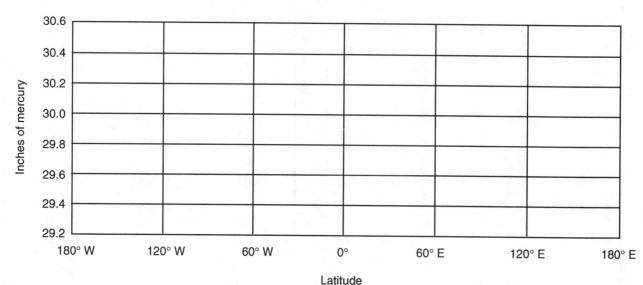

name   section   date

Review and Study Questions

1. Define what is meant by *air pressure*.

2. Explain the difference between *thermally induced* pressure and *mechanically induced* (airflow; convergence and divergence) pressure.

3. Compare the operating principles of the mercury barometer and the aneroid barometer.

4. Describe a barograph.

5. List the corrections necessary for accurate readings from the mercury barometer and give the reasons why each correction is necessary.

   a.

   b.

   c.

   d.

6. Which of the above corrections are necessary for an aneroid barometer?

7. *Station pressure* includes all corrections except one. Which one is omitted?

8. What is the *rate* by which atmospheric pressure decreases with increasing altitude in the lower atmosphere?

9. Specifically where is the highest mean pressure for January found on the earth's surface?

10. Specifically where is the lowest mean sea-level pressure for January found on the earth's surface?

11. Specifically where is the lowest mean pressure for July found on the earth's surface?

12. Several areas have about the same mean high pressure in July. There is something about the locations of all five of these areas that is essentially identical. What is the common nature of these areas with the same mean July high pressure?

13. A *daily pressure cycle* seems to exist. It is especially clear in the lower latitudes, but tends to be overpowered by other factors in the middle latitudes. What is this daily pressure cycle?

14. Why is a knowledge of barometric characteristics (the pressure tendency and net change in pressure) perhaps the most useful single piece of information for *short-term* weather forecasting?

15. What is a *cyclone*?

16. What is an *anticyclone*?

17. What kind of forecasting help is provided by upper-air constant-pressure charts (also called pressure-contour charts and standard pressure-surface charts)?

chapter 7

WIND and THE GLOBAL CIRCULATION

Like air pressure, wind is an *element* of weather and climate as well as a *control* or determinant of weather and climate. The speed of the wind may be highly significant as an element of weather. There is considerable difference between calm conditions and gale-force conditions. Winds associated with special storms, such as tornadoes and hurricanes, may not be everyday occurrences, but they are of paramount importance when they do occur. Onshore winds occurring with high tides may have profound effects on coastal areas. The effect wind has of reducing temperatures to a lower equivalent value (the **wind-chill factor**) can be dangerous when the temperature is low. The effect wind has of removing body heat and increasing the rate of evaporation can be a source of great relief on warm or hot days when the relative humidity is high.

As a weather and climate control, the wind transports heat and moisture from one region to another. The direction of the wind may tell us, therefore, that the air is coming from a warm or a cold source region or from a dry or a humid source region. Expected *changes* in wind direction tell us something about the changes in temperature and humidity we might expect.

Because wind is primarily the result of differences in air pressure, it is difficult (even unreasonable) to separate these two elements. This becomes especially true when we attempt to explain weather and climate phenomena. Pressure differences produce wind, and wind induces pressure differences. Winds may vary in scale, as a result of the differences in scale of pressure fields, from purely local winds to regional winds to the global or planetary winds that encompass the earth.

Winds are always *named* according to the direction *from which* they come, even though they are frequently *described* in terms of the direction in which they are blowing. Thus, a wind blowing towards the southwest is named a northeast wind. Any such wind may also have a geographic name, such as *trade wind*. Also, all wind symbols (arrows, wind shafts) point in the direction the wind is moving. The one exception is the arrow of a wind vane, which points *into* the wind and, therefore, *opposite* to the direction the wind is blowing.

As a horizontal flow of air from areas of high pressure to areas of lower pressure, wind is influenced by numerous forces. The net result of these several forces, as far as surface winds are concerned, is a direction that will be at an angle to the pressure gradient force. The pressure gradient force is always at an angle of 90 degrees to the isobars. Measured *from the isobars*, the angle of the wind will average 10 degrees to 20 degrees over the oceans and 20 degrees to 45 degrees over land. The wind angle is nearer to 20 degrees over smooth land surfaces and nearer to 45 degrees over rough terrain.

There are several ways in which winds may be classified according to their various characteristics. They may be classified according to their speed or force (the Beaufort scale), their region of origin (arctic, polar, tropical, maritime, etc.), their direction of flow (north, south, south-southeast, etc.), or their magnitude—the size of the area they affect. In terms of *magnitude*, the three classes of winds include the **primary circulations** (also called planetary, or global, winds), the **secondary circulations** (which include large regional winds such as the Asian monsoon and other quasi-monsoonal winds, the winds associated with cyclones and anticyclones, and the winds associated with weather fronts), and the **tertiary circulations**. The tertiary circulations include smaller-scale regional winds and purely local winds. These tertiary winds include such winds as the *chinook* of North America, the *norther* of the Texas–Gulf of Mexico area, the *Santa Ana* of southern California, the *foehn* of the European Alps, the *bora* of the Adriatic shores of Yugoslavia, the *etesian* winds of the Aegean–Mediterranean area, the *mistral* of southern France, the *pampero* of Argentina, the *sirocco* of northern Africa and southern Europe, and many, many others. Simple land and sea breezes or mountain and valley breezes are also examples of the tertiary circulations.

In the following section of this chapter, we will look at the relationship of the wind to the temperature we feel on exposed skin.

The Wind-Chill Factor and Equivalent Temperatures

Because wind removes the heated layer of air near the body, the effect of the wind is to *reduce* the environmental temperature to a lower value. This lowered value that we feel is the **sensible temperature** or the wind-chill **equivalent temperature**. The wind-chill factor (K) is a measure of the quantity of heat, in kilogram calories (kcal), that can be lost to the air in one hour from an exposed surface of one square meter ($K = $ kcal/ m^2/ hr). Wind speeds (v) are in meters per second (m/s) and the dry-bulb temperature (Td) is in degrees Celsius. Shade is assumed and evaporation is disregarded. The calculation of wind chill also assumes a neutral skin temperature of 33°C (91.4°F) and a constant (k) of 10.45 for cooling by radiation and conduction. The wind-chill factor is found by the equation:

$$K = (\sqrt{v \cdot 100} - v + k)(33 - Td)$$

Thus, for a wind of 18 m/s at a temperature of 5°C the wind-chill factor is 970 kcal per square meter per hour:

$$K = (\sqrt{18 \cdot 100} - 18 + 10.45)(33 - 5)$$

$$K = (42.4 - 18 + 10.45)(28)$$

$$K = 34.85 \times 28$$

$$K = 975.8 \text{ kcal/m}^2/\text{hr}$$

A value of 400 K produces a sensation of cool; 600 K is very cool; 800 K is cold; 1000 K is very cold; 1200 K is bitterly cold; 1400 K will freeze exposed skin; and 2000 K will freeze facial flesh in one minute! A K value of 200 is quite pleasant, 100 K is warm, and a value of 50 K will feel hot.

The wind-chill factor is more frequently expressed in terms of the *equivalent temperature*—the temperature equivalent to a combination of actual temperature and wind speed. Table 26 in Appendix A shows the wind-chill equivalent temperatures for various temperature–wind speed combinations. You will need the above information and Table 4, Squares and Square Roots, (in Appendix A) for Exercise 7.9. Square roots of numbers larger than 100 may be found from the following:

$$\sqrt{100x} = 10\sqrt{x}$$

$$\sqrt{1000x} = 10\sqrt{10x}$$

Note also that each meter per second is equivalent to almost 2¼ miles per hour (2.237 MPH). At the bottom of Table 16 in Appendix A are the exact conversion factors for meters per second, miles per hour, and knots.

name   section   date

Exercises

WIND DIRECTION AND FLOW

7.1   Sketch in the circulation of a *land breeze* and a *sea breeze* in the appropriate diagrams below. Use a series of short arrows to show the complete circulation in each case. Indicate surface high- and low-pressure areas, in words, in each case.

   a.   Daytime   **b.**   Nighttime

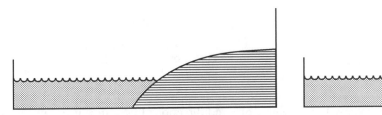

7.2   Sketch in the circulation of the *mountain breeze* and the *valley breeze* in the cross-sectional views of a mountain valley below. Use a series of short arrows to show this circulation.

   a.   Daytime   **b.**   Nighttime

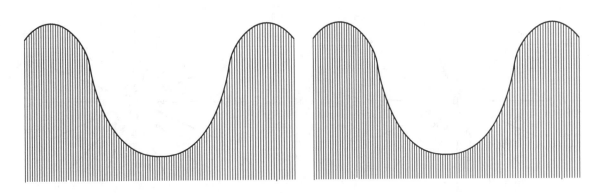

   c.   The above cross-sectional views show the *sides* of the valley. What is the direction of the breeze along the *valley floor*

   1.   in the daytime?

   2.   in the nighttime?

   d.   What processes and forces are responsible for the mountain breeze and the valley breeze?

name   section   date

7.3 For each of the weather map wind symbols given below, give the wind direction and the wind speed.

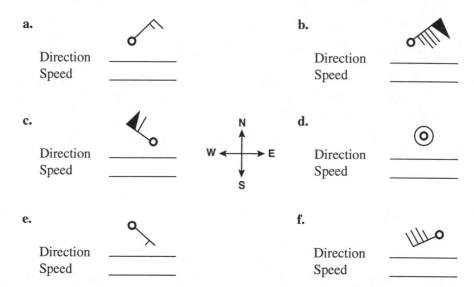

a.

Direction _____
Speed   _____

b.

Direction _____
Speed   _____

c.

Direction _____
Speed   _____

d.

Direction _____
Speed   _____

e.

Direction _____
Speed   _____

f.

Direction _____
Speed   _____

7.4 In each of the two diagrams below, show the *sequence* of wind directions that will illustrate *veering* and *backing* wind shifts. In each diagram, the first wind direction is already numbered as "1" (a wind from the west). Continue to number the wind directions in each example, in sequence from the first position.

a. Veering Wind

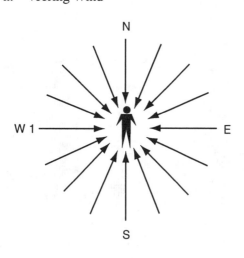

b. Backing Wind

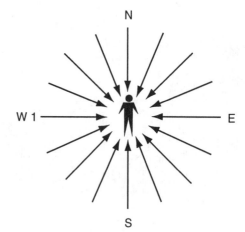

c. How would you describe the *direction* of the wind shift for a veering wind and a backing wind (in words, without using compass directions)?

name   section   date

7.5   Wind frequency percentages for Boston, Massachusetts and Key West, Florida, are given below. Prepare a wind-frequency diagram (wind rose) for each place. The percentage figure for *calm* should be placed inside the inner circle.

Boston		Key West
8	N	10
6	NE	19
9	E	28
4	SE	25
7	S	6
24	SW	4
24	W	2
18	NW	5

a.   Boston   **b.**   Key West

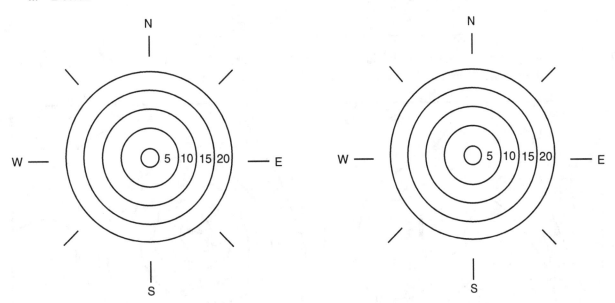

c.   How does your wind rose for Boston relate to the global or planetary wind zones?

d.   How does your wind rose for Key West relate to the global or planetary wind zones?

e.   The above data and wind roses are *annual average* wind frequency information. *Monthly average* wind-rose charts are available from the U.S. Navy Oceanographic Office for the ocean areas. These pilot charts present monthly wind roses for each five degrees of latitude and longitude for each ocean. How would such pilot-chart information be of value to sailors?

name   section   date

7.6 The following map shows a cyclone and an anticyclone in the Northern Hemisphere and, below the line representing the equator, a cyclone and an anticyclone in the Southern Hemisphere. Show the wind-field pattern that should result from each pressure field shown. Use many short arrows, about ½ in. long and spaced no more than about ½ in. apart. This will show the *wind-flow pattern* that should exist within and between each pressure cell within and between hemispheres.

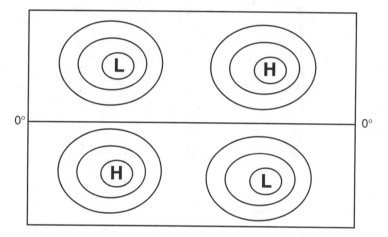

7.7 Show the *wind-flow pattern* that should result from the pressure field shown on the map below. Use many short arrows, about ½ in. long, spaced no farther apart than about 1 in.

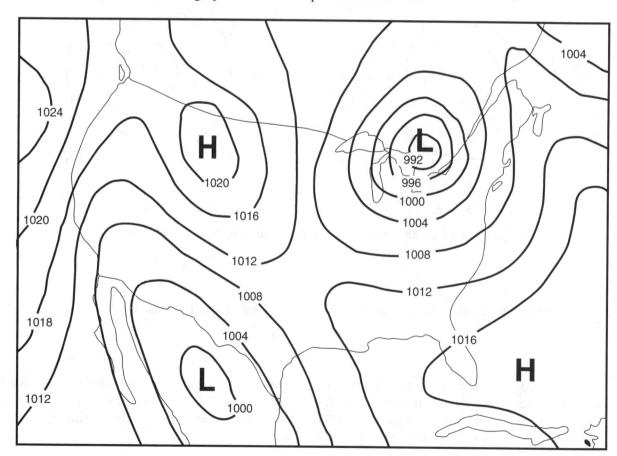

name   section   date

7.8 Based on Table 27 in Appendix A, what are the equivalent temperatures (sensible temperatures) for:

    a.   40°F and 25-MPH wind _____

    b. –30°F and 15-MPH wind _____

    c.   10°F and 25-MPH wind _____

    d. –50°F and 40-MPH wind _____

    e.   0°F and 35-MPH wind _____

    f. Regardless of the actual temperature, the reduction of equivalent temperatures essentially stops beyond a wind speed of _____ .

7.9 Calculate the wind-chill factor from the following facts. Be sure to show all calculations in the spaces provided, place answers on the lines provided, and label all answers.

    a. –20°C (–4°F) and a wind speed of 16 m/s (36 MPH).

_____

    b. –10°C (14°F) and a wind speed of 23 m/s (51 MPH).

_____

    c. –5°C (23°F) and a wind speed of 12 m/s (27 MPH).

_____

name   section   date

WIND SPEED AND THE PRESSURE GRADIENT

7.10 The following is a list of **average pressure gradients** between certain cities:

Omaha and Chicago	0.8 mb per 100 mi
Chicago and Cleveland	3.2 mb per 100 mi
Cleveland and New York	1.4 mb per 100 mi
New York and Boston	2.8 mb per 100 mi

The pressure gradient average of 0.8 mb/100 mi between Omaha and Chicago produces an average wind speed of 6 MPH in the region between the two cities. If it is assumed that the average wind speed between cities is proportional to the pressure gradient, what is the probable wind speed between the other cities? Show all calculations, in a logical sequence, in the spaces below. Label each answer and place answers on the lines provided.

a. Between Chicago and Cleveland

_____

b. Between Cleveland and New York

_____

c. Between New York and Boston

_____

name   section   date

GLOBAL WIND, PRESSURE, AND CIRCULATION

7.11 The area inside the circle below represents the earth's surface. The region outside the circle represents a cross-sectional view of the lower atmosphere. Show the global pressure zones, the surface wind zones, and the general circulation of the lower atmosphere. The earth *is* rotating (so the Coriolis effect should be in evidence). However, you are to assume a uniform earth surface, such as entirely covered with water, so that there are no land and water contrasts. Follow the directions carefully.

   a. Inside the circle, draw in the idealized global pattern of surface *wind zones*, using a series of arrows to show *both* the direction and the deflection—caused by the Coriolis effect—of the wind.

   b. To the *right* of the circle, label each of the *pressure zones* and each of the *wind zones*. These names must be written in precise alignment with the latitudes of the pressure and wind zones on your diagram.

   c. Just outside the circle on the *left* side (the cross-sectional view of the troposphere), draw a cross-sectional view of the *tricellular model* of the general circulation of the lower atmosphere. Use a series of short arrows that will show where the air is rising and descending, and the direction of the wind flow aloft and parallel to the surface. Do this on the *left* side of the diagram from the North Pole to the South Pole.

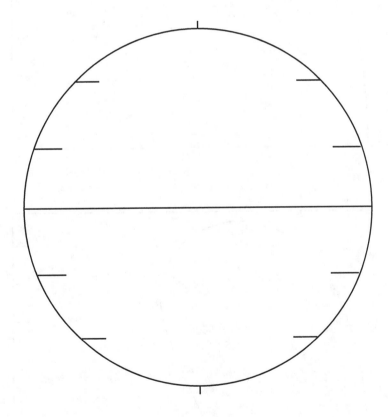

name   section   date

7.12 The previous exercise was based on an important assumption: a uniform earth surface. Your diagram, therefore, represents the *annual average* situation where the effects of land and water contrasts are balanced out. A hypothetical continent (it could be North America), surrounded by ocean, is introduced in the *seasonal* diagrams below. The effect of land and water contrasts is greatest in the middle latitudes during the extreme seasons. Show the seasonal pattern of pressure and wind on these two diagrams.

First show the seasonal *pressure* pattern by sketching *isobars*. Draw enough to show the pattern, but not too many. Do not bother to label the isobars, but do label the pressure field with *H*s for highs and *L*s for lows. Then show the seasonal *wind* pattern, using arrows.

(a) January:

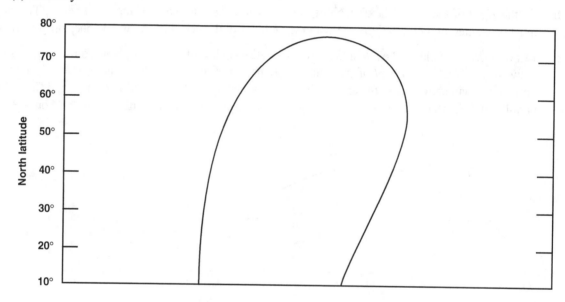

(b) July:

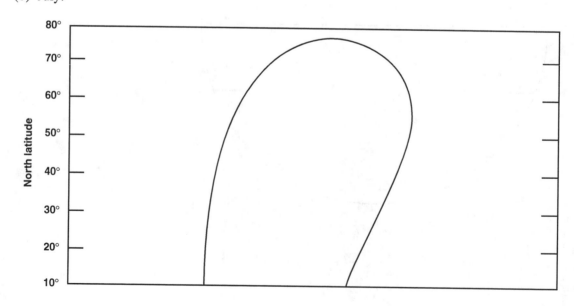

name   section   date

c. How and why does the January pattern (in Exercise 7.12a) differ from the annual average pattern shown in Exercise 7.11?

d. How and why does the July pattern (in Exercise 7.12b) differ from the annual average pattern shown in Exercise 7.11?

e. If the January and July patterns were repeated for the Southern Hemisphere (as it actually exists with regard to land-mass and ocean distributions), would these seasonal patterns differ much from the annual average shown in Exercise 7.11? Why?

f. If you assume that the hypothetical continents shown in the diagrams of this exercise actually were in eastern Asia, how would the change in the pressure and wind patterns from January to July represent the Asian **monsoon**?

7.13 Using the conversion factors found at the bottom of Table 16 in Appendix A, convert the following:

a. 10 knots   = _____ MPH

b. 64 knots   = _____ MPH

c. 34 knots   = _____ MPH

d. 10 MPH   = _____ knot

e. 100 MPH   = _____ knots

f. 10 meters per second = _____ knots

g. 10 meters per second = _____ MPH

name   section   date

Review and Study Questions

1. List the factors (or forces) that account for and explain wind direction and speed.

   a.

   b.

   c.

   d.

2. Which of the above factors is probably the *most fundamental?*

3. The Coriolis effect varies according to *two* considerations. What are these two factors, and how does each influence the degree to which the Coriolis effect causes wind deflection?

4. How does *friction* affect the speed and direction of wind?

5. Describe the air-flow circulation from anticyclones and into cyclones in each hemisphere.

6. What is the Beaufort scale? What is a Beaufort force number? What purposes does the Beaufort scale serve?

7. Describe Buys-Ballot's Law (the law of storms).

chapter *8*

MOISTURE IN THE ATMOSPHERE

Water is unique in that it is extremely abundant in all three states (gas, solid, and liquid) under the normal range of temperatures and pressures found in the troposphere and on the earth's surface. Water vapor, an invisible, odorless, and tasteless gas, varies greatly in amount from place to place and, in a given place, from one moment to another. It ranges in amount from zero to nearly 5% of the total of all gases of the atmosphere, with a global average of about 1%.

Water and the processes related to it contribute to the heating and cooling of the atmosphere through the absorption and release of heat energy and, therefore, affect the global heat budget. The processes that put water from the earth's surface into the atmosphere are closely related to the previous topics of solar radiation, temperature, air pressure, and wind.

The relative humidity of air depends on the temperature and the amount of water vapor in the air and determines how we feel as well as the amount of precipitable water for the support of storms. Water may readily change its state, with the vapor condensing into droplets or ice crystals which may form raindrops or snowflakes. The occurrence or threat of such precipitation is always a significant aspect of the weather. Weather **radar** (*RA*dio *D*etection *A*nd *R*anging) systems have become a most useful tool in the detection and monitoring of precipitation echoes. Radar "sees" precipitation-size (0.5–1.5 mm) water drops and ice crystals and indicates squall lines and cells and areas of showers and thunderstorms. It provides information about the type, location, height, intensity, change in intensity, and speed of movement of the precipitation echoes.

Calculations to determine the actual amount of water vapor in the air, the dew-point temperature, and the relative humidity are quite simple. Confusion frequently stems, however, from several different terms being used for essentially the same thing. The different terms indicate differences in focus or in the *units* used. *Mixing ratio, specific humidity, absolute humidity,* and *vapor pressure* all refer to the same idea: the *actual* amount of water vapor in the air. They differ in the following ways: The **mixing ratio** (r) deals with the mass of water vapor (mv) per unit mass of *dry* air (ma) (the mass of the air without its water vapor). This is found by using the formula $r = mv/ma$ and is expressed in grams per kilogram of air. **Specific humidity** deals with the mass of water vapor per unit mass of *moist* air (the mass of the air including its water vapor). This is found by using the formula $q = mv/(mv + ma)$. Like the mixing ratio, it is expressed in grams per kilogram of air. Because the mass of water vapor compared to air without its water vapor is always very small, there is little difference in the numerical values of the mixing ratio and specific humidity. Both measures have the advantage of remaining constant despite volume changes due to changes in temperature or pressure. **Absolute humidity,** unlike specific humidity or the mixing ratio, describes the amount of water vapor per unit *volume*, such as grams per cubic meter or grains per cubic foot. **Vapor pressure** is also rather different in that it expresses the amount of water vapor in the air in terms of its partial pressure—the pressure exerted by the water vapor alone—in inches (or millimeters) of mercury. All four of the above terms, however, express the same fundamental idea of an *actual amount* of water vapor in the air. The absolute humidity (dv) may be thought of as the vapor density or concentration per unit volume ($dv = mv/V$).

Because of these four different ways of describing the water-vapor content of air it is necessary to have four different expressions of the capacity (or saturation point) of the air. **Saturation mixing ratios** (r_w), **saturation specific humidities** (q_s), **saturation absolute humidities** (d_s), and **saturation vapor pressures** (e_s) all represent the *maximum* amount of water vapor air can hold at a given temperature regardless of the actual amount held. Each type of saturation point expresses the same idea (capacity). Each differs in the *units* used.

Relative humidity (U) is the actual amount of water vapor in the air expressed as a percentage of the capacity (saturation point) of the air at a given temperature. Relative humidity is found by dividing the actual amount of water vapor in the air by the capacity of that air (in the same units) and multiplying by 100. The **dew-point temperature** is closely interrelated with all these concepts. It is the temperature at which air is, or would be, saturated (given the actual amount of water vapor in the air and the air's actual temperature). The dew point is the temperature at which the relative humidity of air with a given moisture content will be 100% (saturated air). It is a lower value than the actual air temperature whenever the air is less than saturated (holding less water vapor than its capacity). If the air is saturated, the dew point and the actual air temperature will be equal. The dew point is usually taken as the temperature at which condensation will occur. The *difference* between the actual temperature of the air and its dew-point temperature is called the **temperature–dew-point spread.** This spread, if plotted on a map and depicted by isopleths, will show the **dew-point depression field.** For surface data, the smaller the spread, the more likely the occurrence of low-level condensation. As the dew-point spread approaches zero, the potential for the development of low-level clouds or **fog** becomes greater. The spread is, therefore, directly related to the relative humidity: the smaller the spread, the higher the relative humidity.

The following is a list of some symbols and formulas related to water vapor:

DEFINITIONS OF SYMBOLS

$$
\begin{aligned}
r &= \text{mixing ratio} \\
r_w &= \text{saturation mixing ratio} \\
q &= \text{specific humidity} \\
q_s &= \text{saturation specific humidity} \\
dv &= \text{absolute humidity}
\end{aligned}
$$

$$
\begin{aligned}
d_s &= \text{saturation absolute humidity} \\
e &= \text{vapor pressure} \\
e_s &= \text{saturation vapor pressure} \\
U &= \text{relative humidity} \\
ma &= \text{mass of dry air} \\
mv &= \text{mass of water vapor} \\
V &= \text{volume} \\
p &= \text{pressure} \\
T &= \text{absolute temperature} \\
Tdew &= \text{temperature of the dewpoint}
\end{aligned}
$$

FORMULAS

$$
\begin{aligned}
\text{Mixing ratio} &= mv/ma \\
\text{Specific humidity} &= mv/(mv + ma) \\
\text{Absolute humidity} &= mv/V
\end{aligned}
$$

Relative humidity (U):

$$
\begin{aligned}
U &= 100 \, r/r_w \\
U &= 100 \, q/q_s \\
U &= 100 \, dv/d_s \\
U &= 100 \, e/e_s
\end{aligned}
$$

Therefore:

$$
\begin{aligned}
r &= r_w U \\
q &= q_s U \\
dv &= d_s U \\
e &= e_s U
\end{aligned}
$$

Other relationships:

$$
\begin{aligned}
e &= (r/0.622 + r)p \\
e_s &= (r_w/0.622 + r_w)p \\
dv &= 217e/T \\
q &= 622e/p - 0.377e \\
r &= 622e/p - e
\end{aligned}
$$

Rain Gauges

Rainfall often occurs in relatively small amounts that are difficult to measure accurately. A standard rain gauge solves this problem. The rainfall is collected by a funnel and empties into a collecting cylinder with a smaller diameter. The smaller cylinder increases the height (H) of the water level for ease and accuracy of measurement. The depth of the rainfall (P) is then found by the formula

$$P = H(d/D)^2$$

where d is the inside diameter of the collecting cylinder and D is the inside diameter of the top of the funnel.

If 2 in. of rainfall is measured *in a cylinder* that has a 1.5-in. inner diameter, collected from a funnel with a 4-in. diameter, the depth of the precipitation is calculated as follows:

$$P = 2 \,(1.5/4)^2$$

$$P = 2 \times 0.141$$

$$P = 0.28 \text{ inches}$$

A measuring stick, or the collecting cylinder itself, may be calibrated for use with the rain gauge so that this calculation does not have to be made every time rain is collected. A narrow piece of redwood, which shows water discoloration clearly, is ideal for this purpose. The calibration of the measuring stick is found from the relationship:

$$k = \frac{1}{(d/D)^2}$$

where k is the factor for relating 1 in. of precipitation to the number of inches on the measuring stick.

In the above example, $(d/D)^2 = 0.141$, and $1/0.141 = 7.1$. Thus, a measurement of 7.1 in. on the measuring stick is required to equal 1 in. of precipitation. For marking the calibration on the measuring stick, it follows that, on the stick,

7.100 in. = 1.00 in. of rainfall; therefore,

0.710 in. = 0.10 in. of rainfall; therefore,

0.071 in. = 0.01 in. of rainfall.

The Temperature-Humidity Index (THI)

Chapter 7 showed that the wind influences how people feel relative to the actual temperature. Wind speeds and temperatures combine to produce lower values of sensible temperature. Humidity also influences how people feel relative to the actual temperature.

The **temperature-humidity index** brings these two factors together, in a single index number, as a measure of relative comfort or discomfort. Indeed, the THI was originally called the discomfort index! A statistical sample of the population working in offices was evaluated in terms of their feelings about their relative comfort or discomfort under a full range of temperature and humidity combinations. These results were used to establish the proportions of the sample that experienced various degrees of comfort or discomfort for the full range of possible temperature-humidity combinations (the full range of possible index numbers).

It was found that most people are comfortable when the THI value is 60 to 65. With a THI of 75, about 50% of the population was uncomfortable. Above a THI of 80, most people will feel uncomfortable (with some feeling more discomfort than others and some feeling less). Nearly everyone feels discomfort and many feel acute discomfort when the THI reaches 85. These discomfort proportions for the index numbers were derived from office workers, inside without air conditioning. They do not consider the effects of direct sunshine or wind flow on people outdoors. However, THI values in the range of 80 to 85 have been used as the basis of decisions to close some offices and dismiss the workers.

The temperature-humidity index is found as follows:

$$\text{THI} = 0.4 \,(T + T\!dew) + 15$$

If the temperature is 90°F and the dew point is 80° F (relative humidity would be 73%), then

$$\text{THI} = 0.4 \,(90 + 80) + 15$$

$$\text{THI} = 0.4 \,(170) + 15$$

$$\text{THI} = 68 + 15$$

$$\text{THI} = 83$$

Just about everyone would feel uncomfortable at this THI.

name   section   date

Exercises

8.1 a. Label every arrow in the following diagram by the name of the *process* each arrow represents.

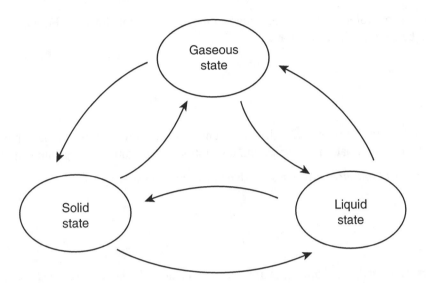

b. Very close to the process name you just placed on the arrows in Exercise 8.1a, write *warming* or *cooling* to show the effect of that process on the immediate environment in which the process takes place.

c. Explain why energy (heat) must be absorbed or released by water for an environmental warming or cooling effect to occur.

d. How much energy (heat) is absorbed or released in each of the above processes, and in each process, what is that energy called?

e. Describe the effects of energy (heat) absorbed or released by water on the average speed of the water molecules. Compare the average speed of water molecules in each state of water.

name   section   date

8.2 Use Figure 8.1, The Water Cycle (hydrologic cycle) to answer the following questions.

    a. Label on the diagram all the *forms* of water shown: ice and snow, freshwater lake, river, seawater, clouds, rain, and fog.

    b. What forms of water might *also* be found in the environment shown in Figure 8.1 (forms that are too small to be depicted in the diagram)?

    c. Label all the arrows in Figure 8.1 that represent the *processes* involved in the water cycle: evaporation, condensation, sublimation, transpiration, respiration, precipitation, and groundwater flowage.

    d. What kinds of *biological* processes are dependent on the water cycle?

    e. What kinds of *geological* processes are a consequence of the hydrologic cycle?

    f. Figure 8.1 shows the major natural reservoirs that hold the water. The volume of water in each of these reservoirs is given below in cubic meters.

Oceans	$1350 \times 10^{15} m^3$
Glaciers and polar ice	$29 \times 10^{15} m^3$
Underground aquifers	$8.4 \times 10^{15} m^3$
Lakes and rivers	$.2 \times 10^{15} m^3$
The atmosphere	$.013 \times 10^{15} m^3$
The biosphere	$.0006 \times 10^{15} m^3$

    1. Calculate the percentage of the total for water held by the oceans. _____ (1)

    2. Calculate the percentage of the total for water held by glaciers and polar ice. _____ (2)

    3. Calculate the water held in the atmosphere as a percentage of *all non-ocean* water. _____ (3)

name   section   date

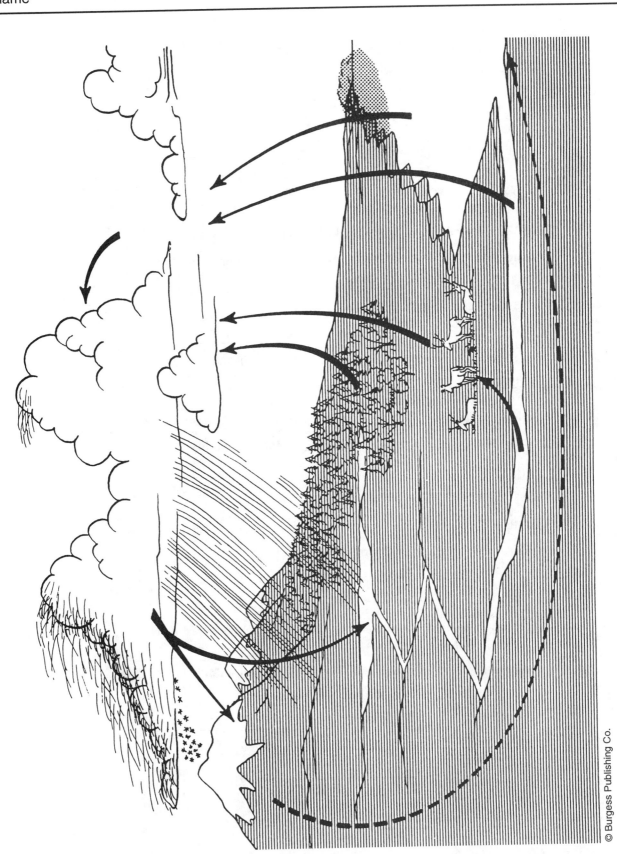

Figure 8.1 The Water Cycle (for Exercise 8.2).

name   section   date

8.3 Using Table 12 in Appendix A, fill in the blanks for each of the following:

Air temperature	Water vapor (gr/ft³)	Relative humidity
5°F	0.40	_____
20°F	0.40	_____
40°F	1.43	_____
60°F	_____	25%
80°F	_____	70%

8.4 Using Table 13 in Appendix A, fill in the blanks for each of the following:

Air temperature	Water vapor (g/m³)	Relative humidity
–5°C	3.0	_____
5°C	3.0	_____
10°C	3.0	_____
15°C	_____	40%
20°C	_____	65%

8.5 Using Table 11 in Appendix A, fill in the blanks for each of the following:

Air temperature	Water vapor (g/kg)	Relative humidity
0°F	0.2	_____
15°F	1.4	_____
25°F	1.4	_____
40°F	_____	84%
60°F	_____	40%
85°F	_____	90%

8.6 Using Table 10 in Appendix A, which contains saturation vapor pressures in the second column, fill in the blanks for each of the following:

Air temperature	Water vapor (in. Hg)	Relative humidity
15°F	0.070	_____
25°F	0.070	_____
55°F	0.222	_____
75°F	_____	65%
90°F	_____	40%
95°F	_____	78%

name   section   date

8.7 Using the psychrometric tables in Appendix A, Tables 9 and 10, fill in the following blanks.

Air temperature	Wet-bulb depression	Relative humidity	Dew point	Vapor pressure
20°F	5°	_____	_____	_____
45°F	6°	_____	_____	_____
60°F	3°	_____	_____	_____
85°F	10°	_____	_____	_____
25°F	_____	_____	−3°	_____
70°F	_____	_____	61°	_____
30°F	_____	16%	_____	_____
50°F	_____	27%	_____	_____
_____	16°	50%	_____	_____
_____	9°	56%	_____	_____
_____	5°	_____	40°	_____
_____	19°	_____	39°	_____

8.8 In the space below, calculate the amount of water vapor in the air as measured in each of the following units. Place your answers on the first set of lines and write the name of each answer (what it is called) on the second line. The mass of air under consideration has a temperature of 60°F and the wet bulb reads 52°F.

a. inches of mercury   _____   _____

b. grams per kilogram   _____   _____

c. grains per cubic foot   _____   _____

d. grams per cubic meter   _____   _____

8.9 If the wet-bulb temperature of saturated air is 85°F, what is the vapor pressure of the air?

name   section   date

8.10 a. Plot the data from Table 11 in Appendix A, Saturation Mixing Ratios, on the following graph. Then draw a curve of the temperature-capacity relationship.

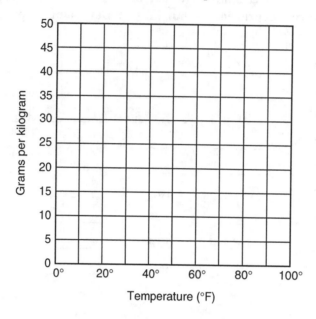

b. What does your curve on the graph in Exercise 8.10a tell you about the rate of change in the capacity of air to hold water vapor at changing temperatures?

8.11 If air has a relative humidity of 40% and contains 3.71 grams of water vapor per kilogram of air, what is the temperature, the dew point, and the saturation mixing ratio of the air? Place your answers on the lines provided and show your calculation in the space below.

a. Temperature of the air   _____

b. Dew-point temperature   _____

c. Saturation mixing rate   _____

8.12 A cool maritime air mass moves into the Pacific Northwest. This air mass has a temperature of 55°F and a relative humidity of 60%. As it moves over the mountains of the northwestern states, this air mass loses 4.20 gm of water vapor per kg of air through condensation and precipitation. It also warms to 65°F as it becomes modified by passing over the warmer land surface.

Using these facts, answer the following questions. Show all calculations in a logical sequence in the space below. Place your answers on the lines provided.

a.   What is the dew-point temperature of the *original* maritime air mass?   _____

b.   What is the dew-point temperature of the *modified* air mass?   _____

c.   What is the relative humidity of the *modified* air mass?   _____

name   section   date

8.13 A cold air mass from Canada has a temperature of 10°F and a relative humidity of 90%. This air mass is moving southeast while another air mass is moving from the Gulf of Mexico toward the northeast. The Gulf air mass has a temperature of 60°F and a relative humidity of 22%.

Using these facts, answer the following questions. Show all calculations in a logical sequence in the space below. Place your answers on the lines provided.

	Canadian	**Gulf**
a. What is the mixing ratio of each air mass?		
b. What is the temperature–dew-point spread of each?		
c. What is the saturation deficit of each air mass?		

d. If these two air masses meet and mix, which one is the most logical source of any precipitation that might result? Why?

name   section   date

8.14 Fill in the information required in the cloud-classification chart below. Three items have been entered for you.

Cloud Family	Code	Cloud Genus	Cloud Abbreviation	Mean Lower Level	Mean Upper Level
		Cirrus	Ci		
High Clouds	C_H				
Middle Clouds					
Low Clouds					
Vertical Clouds					

8.15 Using Tables 22, 23, and 24 in Appendix A, identify each of the following weather map cloud symbols and write its meaning in the space beneath the symbol.

a. 	**b.** 	**c.** 	**d.** 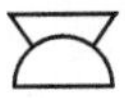
e. 	**f.** 	**g.** 	**h.**
i. 	**j.** 	**k.** 	**l.** 

name   section   date

8.16 The following exercise is to be based on your own observations, identifications, and classification of clouds during a seven-day period. You will need the cloud photographs in your textbook (or any good cloud-identification manuals, charts, or photographs). You are required to make *two* observations and entries each day for seven *consecutive* days. You must try to make each day's observations as close to the same times as those of the previous day. Choose two times of day that are convenient for you. (An example entry is provided at the top of the chart.)

Date	Time	Clouds	Remarks
4/2/96	10:10 A.M.	nimbostratus	rained all morning; windy
	2:35 P.M.	Cu, Ac, Ci	mostly Ac, wm front passed

name   section   date

8.17 a. Plot the monthly mean precipitation data for the following cities on the graph below. Use a different color or line symbol to draw the precipitation curves for each city and label each curve clearly.

	J	F	M	A	M	J	J	A	S	O	N	D	Year
Boston, MA	3.8	3.3	4.0	3.7	3.2	3.4	3.1	3.7	3.4	3.2	3.8	3.5	42.1
St. Louis, MO	2.2	2.3	3.3	3.8	4.1	4.4	3.4	3.4	3.0	2.9	2.7	2.3	37.8
Portland, OR	6.1	4.5	4.3	2.6	2.2	1.7	0.5	0.7	1.8	3.5	5.9	6.7	40.5
San Diego, CA	1.9	2.1	1.6	0.7	0.3	0.1	0.0	0.1	0.2	0.4	0.9	2.0	10.3

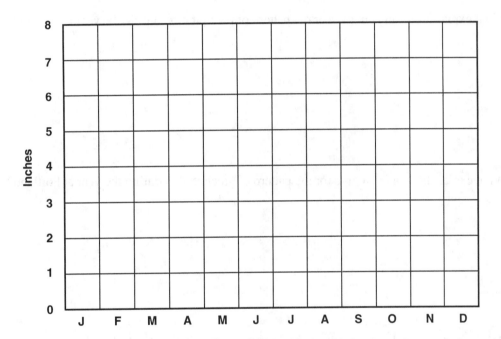

b. How would you describe the seasonal distribution of precipitation of each city?

1. Boston:

2. St. Louis:

3. Portland:

4. San Diego:

c. With the months of April through September considered as the summer or high-sun season, what is the summer precipitation as a percentage of the annual total?

1. Boston:

2. St. Louis:

3. Portland:

4. San Diego:

d. What explanation can you give for the pattern of precipitation during the year at San Diego?

e. What explanation can you give for the pattern of precipitation during the year at Boston?

f. What explanation can you give for the pattern of precipitation during the year at Portland?

g. Boston and Portland have similar annual average precipitation totals, but they have different seasonal distributions. Furthermore, the precipitation during the winter months (November, December, January, and February) averages 30% snow for Boston but only 3.6% snow for Portland. Assuming an average snow/water equivalent ratio of 10:1, what is the annual average snowfall for Boston and for Portland? (Show your calculations.)

Boston _____

Portland _____

name   section   date

8.18 Map 8.1 is the weather map for Thursday, April 12. From the data shown on this map, the *spread* between the temperature and the dew point has been found for every station except those in the southern states. These *T-Tdew* spreads have been plotted on Map 8.2, the work map.

    a. Determine the *T-Tdew* spreads for the southern states and plot these values on Map 8.2. Then, *draw isopleths* for values of 10 degrees (spread) and 20 degrees (spread). Label all isopleths.

    b. What correlation can you discover between the regions with a temperature–dew-point spread of 20 degrees or more and the total cloud cover of stations within those regions?

    c. What, if any, correlation exists between the temperature–dew-point spread and the isobaric pattern of air pressure?

    d. Can you find any correlation between the temperature–dew-point spread and the positions of the weather fronts?

8.19 For this exercise, use *your* map of the temperature–dew-point spread (Map 8.2) prepared in Exercise 8.18. Be sure your isopleths are correct before you begin this exercise. If they are correct, be sure these isopleths are *heavy dark lines*. For this exercise, compare the dew-point depression field (the spread) with the precipitation pattern shown on Map 8.1.

    a. On your map, *outline* the areas receiving precipitation at 7:00 A.M. Simply transfer the outline of the precipitation areas shown on the April 12 weather map to your map of the dew-point depression field.

    b. Very *lightly* shade in the areas of precipitation you just outlined on your map (but do *not* hide your plotted data).

    c. Study the precipitation pattern in relation to the isopleth pattern of the temperature–dew-point spread. Examine the spread values that you plotted on your map. What correlations can you find? How many *separate* regions show a correlation, and *where*, specifically, are these regions?

name   section   date

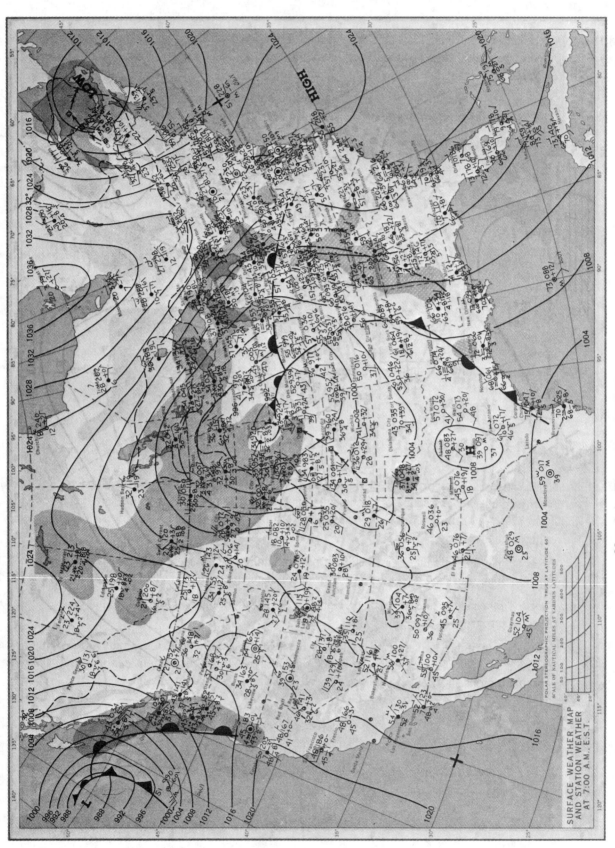

Map 8.1   Thursday, April 12.

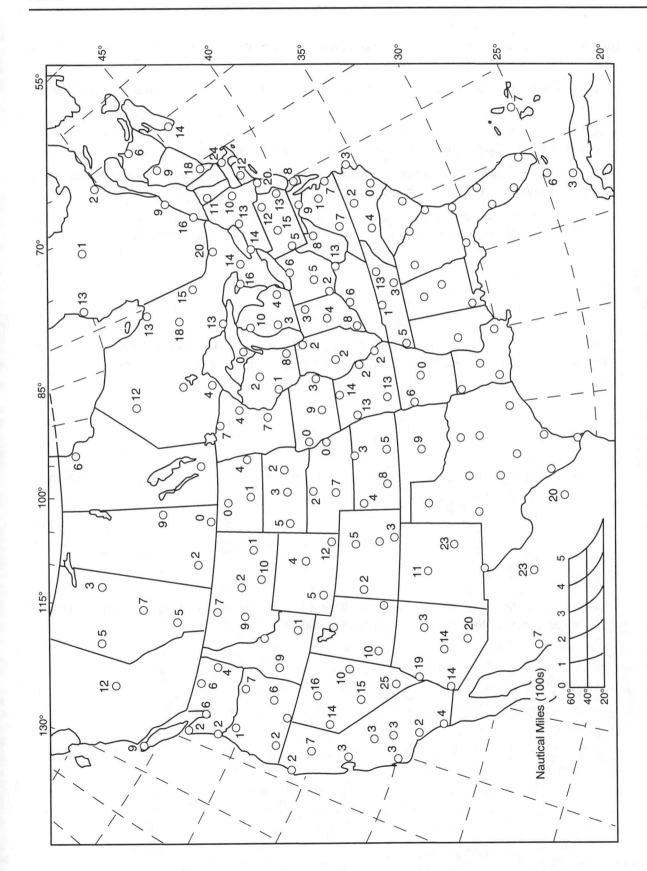

Map 8.2 Work Map for Exercises 8.18 and 8.19.

8.20 This exercise requires the use of the world map of annual precipitation found in your textbook. You are to draw selected *isohyets* on Map 8.3, a blank map of the world.

    a. Draw in the 20-in. (50-cm) annual precipitation isohyet and the 80-in. (200-cm) annual precipitation isohyet.

    b. Using two different colors (or other area symbols), color in the *areas* of 20 in. (50 cm) *or less* annual precipitation and the areas of 80 in. (200 cm) *or more* annual precipitation.

When your map is completed, answer the following questions, which are based on the locational consistency of the global pattern of wet and dry regions.

    c. What generalizations can you make about the locational patterns of arid and semiarid regions with 20 in. (50 cm) or less annual precipitation? (Look for three *different types* of locations.)

    d. What generalizations can you make about the locational patterns of those regions that are very wet with 80 in. (200 cm) or more annual precipitation? (Look for three *different types* of locations.)

    e. Why might a region with 20 in. (50 cm) of rainfall per year be *arid* while another region with 15 in. (40 cm) per year be only *subhumid*?

    f. Why is the eastern horn of Brazil, with 20–40 in. (50–100 cm) of rainfall per year, much drier than northwest Europe, which also has 20–40 in. of rainfall annually?

name   section   date

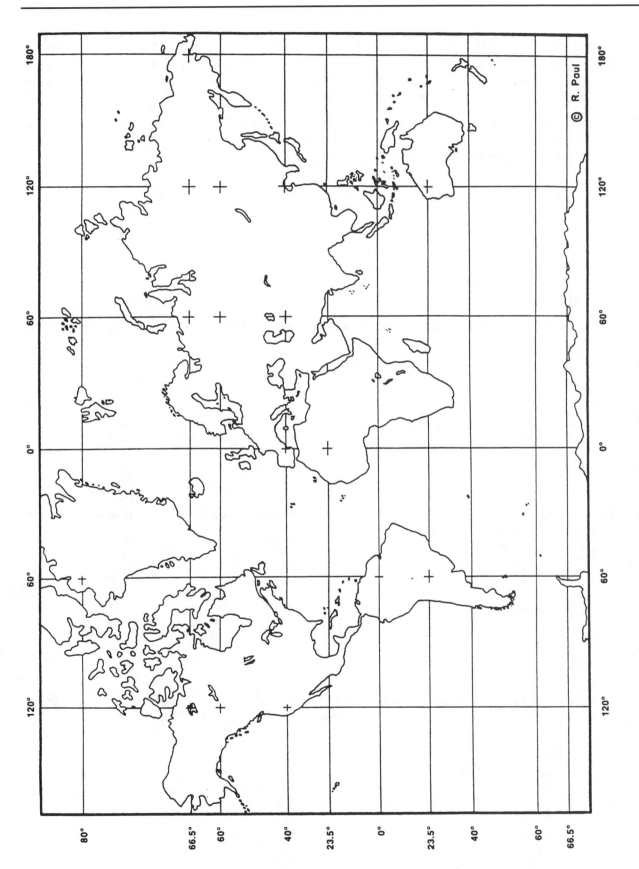

Map 8.3 (for Exercise 8.20).

© R. Paul

8.21 The following exercise will require a rereading of the text at the beginning of this chapter. The text explains how to determine the actual amount of rainfall collected in an uncalibrated funnel-type rain gauge. The text also explains how to calibrate a measuring stick for such a rain gauge. Show all calculations in the spaces provided, and place your answers on the lines.

a. A rain gauge is used to collect a 6-hour rainfall. The rain gauge uses a funnel 5 in. in diameter that empties into an inner rain-collecting cylinder that has an inner diameter of 1.5 in. If the 6-hour rainfall measures 3.2 in. in the cylinder, what is the actual depth of the rainfall?

_____

b. How many inches on a measuring stick, made for the above rain gauge, would be required to equal 1 in. of actual rainfall?

_____

c. Every 0.1 in. of rainfall marked on the above measuring stick would have to be marked how many inches apart on the measuring stick?

_____

d. A funnel with a 6.5-in. diameter is used with a collecting cylinder 2 in. in diameter. If a 12-hr rainfall measures 11.4 in. in the cylinder, what is the actual depth of the 12-hr. rainfall?

name   section   date

8.22 Using Table 14, Radar Chart Symbols, in Appendix A, answer the following questions. Refer to Map 8.4, Radar Summary Chart.

    a. Where do you find a *line* of echoes?   _____
What is the direction and speed of the
line of echoes?   _____

    b. For the area of echoes in Colorado: _____

        What is the echo coverage?   _____

        What is the weather?   _____

        What is the echo intensity?   _____

        What is the intensity trend?   _____

        What is the height of the echo tops?   _____

        What is the direction of the echo movement?   _____

        What is the speed of the echo movement?   _____

    c. How many severe weather watches are there?   _____

    d. Why is there no echo in Michigan?   _____

        Why is there no echo in New York?   _____

        Why is there no echo in Mississippi?   _____

    e. Describe, in your words, *everything* related to the echo cell in Mexico (near the Texas border).

    f. Three small areas of echoes are found in eastern Idaho and northwestern Wyoming. Where did the information about the height of the tops of these echoes come from?

    g. Where are the areas where tornadoes are most likely to occur?

    h. Where do you think there are weather fronts?

    i. Exactly *what* does weather radar detect?

name   section   date

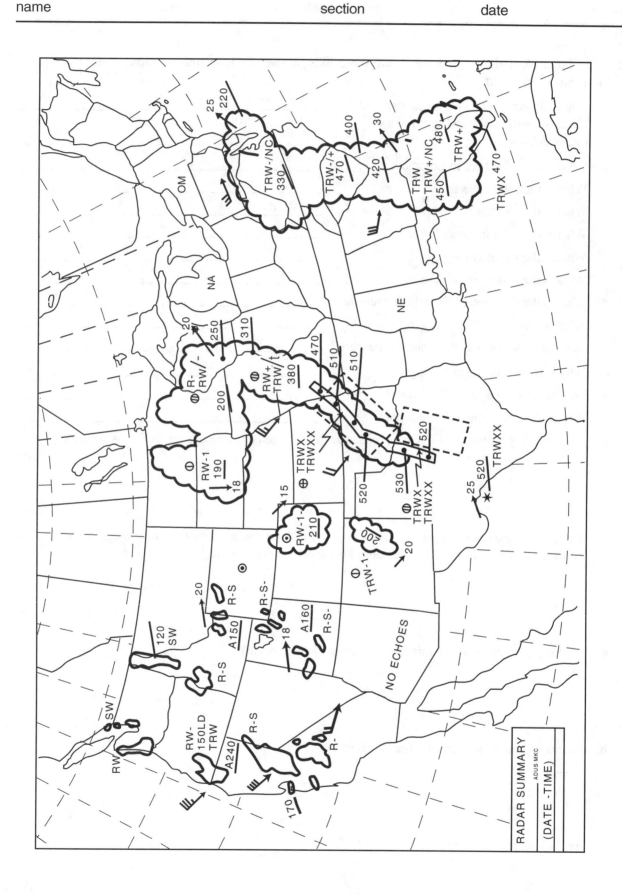

Map 8.4 Radar Summary Chart (for Exercise 8.22).

name   section   date

8.23 Derive the *temperature–humidity index,* and answer the questions, for the following situations. You should reread the text at the beginning of this chapter before you start. Show all calculations and place your answers on the lines provided.

a.   The temperature is 70°F and the dew point is 70°F.

_____THI

What proportion of department store clerks might be expected to feel some discomfort?

_____

b.   The temperature is 88°F and the dew point is 84°F.

_____THI

What proportion of factory workers might be expected to feel discomfort?

_____

c.   The temperature is 98°F and the dew point is 62°F.

_____THI

What proportion of office workers might be expected to feel discomfort?

_____

d.   The temperature is 96°F and the dew point is 89°F.

_____THI

What proportion of students might be expected to feel discomfort?

_____

name   section   date

Review and Study Questions

1. List and briefly explain each of the several factors that affect the *rate of evaporation*.

2. What are the conditions necessary for *condensation* to occur?

3. Briefly explain each of the four major cooling processes in relation to condensation.

4. There are four major ways that air is forced to rise. The cooling, condensation, and precipitation that result give us four major types of precipitation, defined by the cause of uplift of the air rather than by the form of the precipitation. What are these four ways in which air is uplifted and these four types of resultant precipitation?

5. What are the *sources* of condensation nuclei?

6.   Two theories are usually offered to explain the physical processes that produce raindrops from condensation droplets. Briefly describe these two *raindrop-formation processes*.

7.   Explain the underlying principles of the sling psychrometer. (Not how to use one, but *why* it works; that is, what are the principles involved that allow us to use *thermometers* to determine various humidity facts about air?)

8.   On the subject of *acid precipitation* answer the following questions.

    a.   What is "acid rain"?

    b.   What is the pH of *neutral* water?

    e.   What is the pH of "normal" rain?

    d.   What are the pH's of any two common liquids?

    e.   What are the major *pollutants* that cause acid precipitation?

    f.   What are the various *sources* of these pollutants?

    g.   What are the several effects of acid precipitation on our environment?

chapter 9

ATMOSPHERIC STABILITY and ADIABATICS

The temperature of a gas (or a mixture of gases, such as air) may be changed by the addition or subtraction of heat energy, by a change in pressure, or by both. Temperature changes resulting from the direct or indirect addition or loss of heat energy (diabatic processes) were examined in previous chapters. We will now examine the nature of temperature changes resulting from changes in pressure. Decreases in pressure will cause a parcel of air to expand and become less dense and cooler, while increases in pressure bring about compression of the air and increased density and warming. Convectional, frontal, orographic (topographic), and cyclonic processes cause air to be uplifted, and such uplifted air parcels find themselves moving vertically through surroundings of less and less pressure. Such a parcel of air will expand, and the internal energy used to perform the work of expansion will bring about a decrease in the temperature of the air parcel. This temperature change is directly proportional to the pressure change. Essentially no heat energy is lost by the parcel. Its heat energy is now contained in a larger volume. Descending air reverses the process and is warmed by compression. Such processes, where the temperature change is the result of a pressure change with no loss or addition of heat, are called *adiabatic processes.*

The rate at which adiabatic temperature changes occur depends on phase changes of the water in the air. If air is not saturated, the rate is 5.5°F per 1000 ft. This rate is called the **dry adiabatic lapse rate.** The dry adiabatic lapse rate does not mean the air is dry—it may contain a large amount of water vapor. It simply means that the air is *not saturated* at its temperature. If such a parcel of air rises and expands, it will cool at this dry adiabatic rate until the temperature

falls to the dew point. Condensation will then occur, which will release the latent heat of condensation. This latent heat, added to the air parcel while condensation goes on, will *reduce* the rate of cooling. This lower rate of temperature change will apply to any continued uplift and expansion. Because this cooling rate is not the result of expansion alone but is lowered by the addition of latent heat, it is not a purely adiabatic process. It is a pseudo-adiabatic process. The rate is usually called the **moist adiabatic lapse rate** (also called the **wet adiabatic lapse rate, saturated adiabatic lapse rate,** or **pseudo-adiabatic lapse rate**). This rate varies only slightly with the temperature and moisture content of the air and is generally given as 3.2°F per 1000 ft for moderate temperatures in the lower troposphere. This rate of cooling may be slightly higher in polar air, winter air, and the upper troposphere, where less latent heat may be released. It may be slightly lower in the tropics.

Rising air that contains water vapor expands and cools, and may eventually cool to a temperature equal to its dew point. However, the beginning dew-point temperature itself decreases with pressure changes. The expansion results in a greater volume and, therefore, less water vapor per unit of volume and a lowered dew point. The amount of water has not changed; only the temperature and volume density have changed. The rate at which the dew point falls, with rising and cooling air, is usually taken to be 1°F per 1000 ft, up to that altitude where the temperature and the dew point are equal. At this height, any further rise will cool the air below the dew point and start the condensation phase change and the release of the latent heat. Not only does the *moist adiabatic lapse rate* then apply to the parcel of air, but the moist adiabatic rate also becomes the *new* dew-point lapse rate. From this level the dew point must fall at the same rate as the temperature, since the air remains saturated, at least until nearly all the water vapor has been removed from the air.

The altitude or height at which the cooling air (at the *dry* rate) becomes equal to the falling dew point is called the **lifting condensation level** (LCL). This is the altitude at which condensation begins and is therefore the height (*h*) for the *base* of clouds. The lifting condensation level may be found by dividing the *difference* between the temperature and the dew point of air at the beginning of its uplift (*T–Tdew*) by the *difference* in the two rates that apply (the dry adiabatic rate and the dew-point lapse rate). This gives a rate of 4.5°F per 1000 ft (5.5°F minus 1°F per 1000 ft). This is the rate at which the two falling values approach each other for unsaturated rising air. It may be called the **temperature–dew-point approach rate.** If the unit of 1000 ft (used for the rate of change) is divided by 4.5 degrees (the *T–Tdew* approach rate), a factor of 222.22 is obtained. This means that for every single degree of *difference* between the beginning temperature and beginning dew point, the air will have to rise 222.22 ft in order to reduce the difference to zero.

Adiabatic lapse rates (including the moist rate) should not be confused with temperature lapse rates for stationary air. Adiabatic rates apply to a given parcel or mass of air that is ascending or descending *through* the surrounding air. Adiabatic rates apply to such a parcel's internal temperature changes. In Chapter 5, Temperature, we saw that there is a vertical temperature lapse rate for still or "stationary" air.

"Stationary" does not mean there is no wind or motion in the air at all. It simply means there are no *vertical* air currents. This lapse rate varies considerably, but the *average* is given as 3.5°F per 1000 ft, and it is called the **normal temperature lapse rate** (or **average temperature lapse rate**). Because the *actual* temperature lapse rate for stationary air varies widely from the average (from as little as 1°F per 1000 ft to as much as 7°F per 1000 ft), the actual values at a given place and time must be obtained by direct or indirect measurement. Such an actual lapse rate value for stationary air is called an **observed temperature lapse rate.** The observed rate describes the temperatures found at various altitudinal environments within the troposphere and is also referred to as the **environmental temperature lapse rate.** It is *through* this "stationary" temperature environment, with its actual observed temperature lapse rate, that a parcel of air may ascend or descend and undergo dynamic temperature changes by adiabatic processes.

Adiabatic and diabatic lapse rates are negative for upward directions and positive for downward directions. An exception exists for temperature inversions, in which the reverse is true for the observed or environmental lapse rate.

The altitude at which the temperature of expanding air is equal to the temperature of the surrounding (environmental) air is the **level of free convection** (LFC). Any further lifting of air containing water vapor produces instability and tends to produce explosive cloud development from the release of latent heat.

The following summarizes these lapse rates:

Dry adiabatic lapse rate (DALR)	5.5°F/1000 ft	10°C/km	1°C/100 m
Moist adiabatic lapse rate (MALR)	3.2°F/1000 ft	5.8°C/km	.58°C/100 m
Dew-point lapse rate (*Tdew*LR)	1°F/1000 ft (3.2°F/1000 ft above the LCL)	1.8°C/km	.18°C/100 m
Temperature–dew-point approach rate (*T-Tdew*AR)	4.5°F/1000 ft (or 222.22 ft per °F)	8°C/km	.8°C/100 m
Normal (average) temperature lapse rate (LR)	3.5°F/1000 ft	6.5°C/km	.65°C/100 m
Observed (environmental) temperature lapse rate (LR)	Varies widely; obtained by actual measurement.		
Lifting condensation level (LCL)	Obtained by the formula $LCL = (T - Tdew/4.5) \times 1000$. The LCL, therefore, is 222.22 ft per °F.		

Atmospheric Stability

The temperature lapse rates can be used to determine the equilibrium of a parcel of air. The adiabatically determined temperature of a rising parcel of air, relative to the surrounding environmental temperatures, will indicate whether that parcel of air is stable or unstable. If the parcel is warmer (less dense) than the surrounding air it will be unstable and will continue to rise (even if the initial force should cease). If a parcel of air is colder (denser) than the surrounding air it will be stable and will want to return to its original position (if the initial force of uplift ceases).

The illustrations in Figure 9.1 may be helpful. A ball resting inside a bowl is in *absolute stability*. If a force moves the ball it will eventually return to its original position. With a ball balanced on top of an inverted bowl, any force that moves the ball will cause the ball to continue to move and it will *not* return to its original position. This is a case of *absolute instability*. In the third example, a ball resting on a tablet represents *neutral stability*. A force may move the ball, but the ball will stop after the force is removed. The ball will then remain in its new position. Perhaps the most common type of instability is called *conditional instability*. This situation exists when the observed lapse rate for moist air is between the dry and wet adiabatic rates. Such air is stable to begin with, but if some force causes it to rise above the condensation level, the release of latent heat makes the air become warmer than the surrounding air and, therefore, unstable. It is *conditional* because the air must be forced above the condensation level by some external process to become unstable.

The list below summarizes how the observed (environmental) temperature lapse rate, relative to the adiabatic rates, indicates the conditions of atmospheric stability for parcels of air.

The Foehn-Type Wind

The foehn-type wind illustrates nicely the adiabatic principles we have discussed. It is a gusty, warm, dry wind that descends the leeward side of a mountain. The **foehn** is found in the European Alps in the valleys on the north side. Along the eastern slopes of the Rocky Mountains of North America it is called the **chinook.** In early spring, its warmth causes more rapid melting of the snow on the leeward side (the chinook is sometimes called the "snow-eater"). As air rises up the windward side of a mountain it cools, its moisture eventually condenses, and heavy precipitation often occurs (orographic precipitation). As the air descends the leeward side, adiabatic warming due to compression of the subsiding air causes the air to warm and become moisture-absorbent. As a result, the windward sides of mountains may have heavy precipitation while the leeward sides may be extraordinarily dry. Indeed, deserts may be found in the lee of the mountains as a result of this process. Such deserts are called **rain-shadow deserts** as a consequence of their leeward position in the "shadow" of the rainy windward side. The height of the snowline on a mountain often varies because of such winds and the adiabatic process.

Observed lapse rate	<	Dry ALR	=	stability
Observed lapse rate	<	Moist ALR	=	absolute stability
Observed lapse rate	>	Moist ALR	=	instability
Observed lapse rate	>	Dry ALR	=	absolute instability
Observed lapse rate {	<	Dry ALR	=	conditional instability
	>	Moist ALR		
Observed lapse rate {	=	Dry ALR	=	neutral stability
	=	Moist ALR		

Ball in bowl

Absolute stability

Ball balanced on bowl

Absolute instability

Ball resting on table

Neutral stability

FIGURE 9.1

name section date

Exercises

9.1 On the following graph, assuming a ground-level temperature of 68°F and a dew point of 50°F, do the following:

   a. Plot an observed temperature lapse rate of 3°F/1000 ft.

   b. Calculate the LCL and draw a line across the graph to indicate it.

   c. Plot the dry adiabatic lapse rate up to the LCL and plot the moist adiabatic lapse rate from the LCL to 5000 ft.

   d. Plot the dew-point lapse rates up to 5000 ft. (Label all curves and lines *clearly.*)

   e. Calculate the environmental temperatures, adiabatic temperatures of a rising parcel of air, and the difference (+ or −) between these two for every 1000 ft. Place these figures (correct to one decimal place) on the lines provided. Use a plus sign when the adiabatic temperature of the air parcel is higher than the surrounding environmental temperature; use a minus sign when the adiabatic temperature is lower.

   f. What is the stability condition shown?

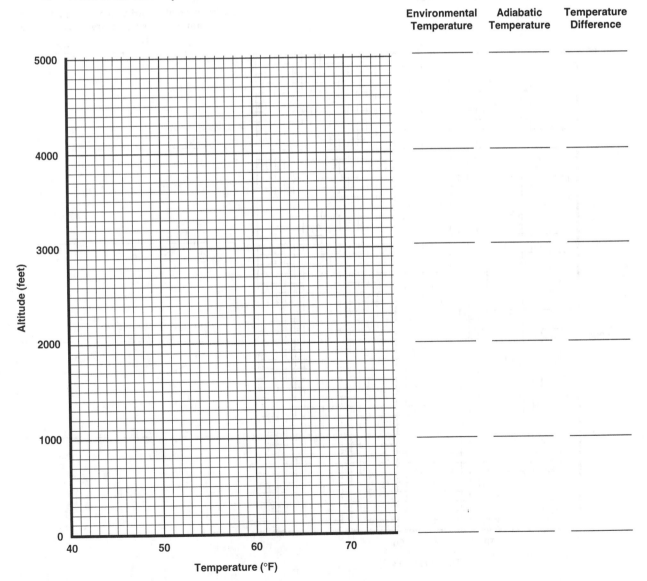

name   section   date

9.2   On the following graph, assuming a ground-level temperature of 70°F and a dew point of 56.5°F, do the following:

   a.   Plot an observed temperature lapse rate of 6.5°F/1000 ft.

   b.   Calculate the LCL and draw a line across the graph to indicate it.

   c.   Plot the dry adiabatic lapse rate up to the LCL and plot the moist adiabatic lapse rate from the LCL to 5000 ft.

   d.   Plot the dew-point lapse rates up to 5000 ft. (Label all curves *clearly.*)

   e.   Calculate the environmental temperatures, adiabatic temperatures of a rising parcel of air, and the difference (+ or –) between these two, for every 1000 ft. Place these figures (correct to one decimal place) on the lines provided. Use a plus sign when the parcel has a higher temperature than the surrounding environmental temperature. Use a minus sign when adiabatic temperature is lower than environmental.

   f.   What is the stability condition shown?

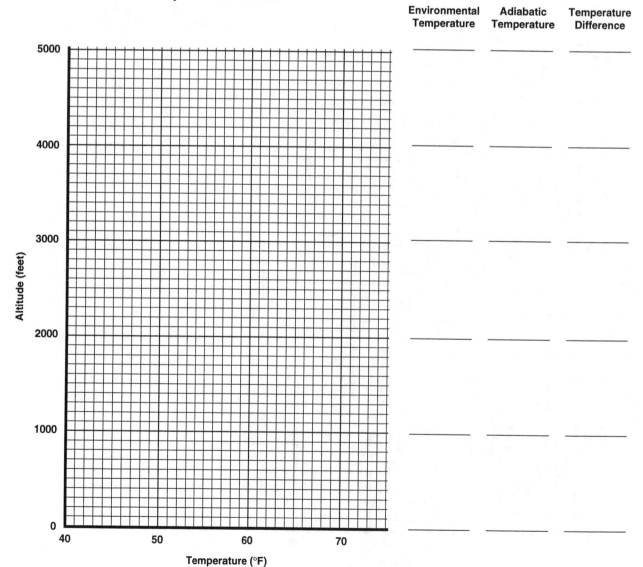

name   section   date

9.3 On the following graph, assuming a ground-level temperature of 73°F and a dew point of 64°F, do the following:

a. Plot an observed temperature lapse rate of 4.5°F/1000 ft.

b. Calculate the LCL and draw a line across the graph to indicate it.

c. Plot the dry adiabatic lapse rate up to the LCL and plot the moist adiabatic lapse rate from the LCL to 5000 ft.

d. Plot the dew-point lapse rates up to 5000 ft. (Label all curves and lines *clearly.*)

e. Calculate the environmental temperatures, adiabatic temperatures of a rising parcel of air, and the difference (+ or −) between these two, for every 1000 ft. Place these figures (correct to one decimal place) on the lines provided. Use a plus sign when the parcel has a higher temperature than the surrounding environmental temperature; use a minus sign when it is lower.

f. What is the stability condition shown?

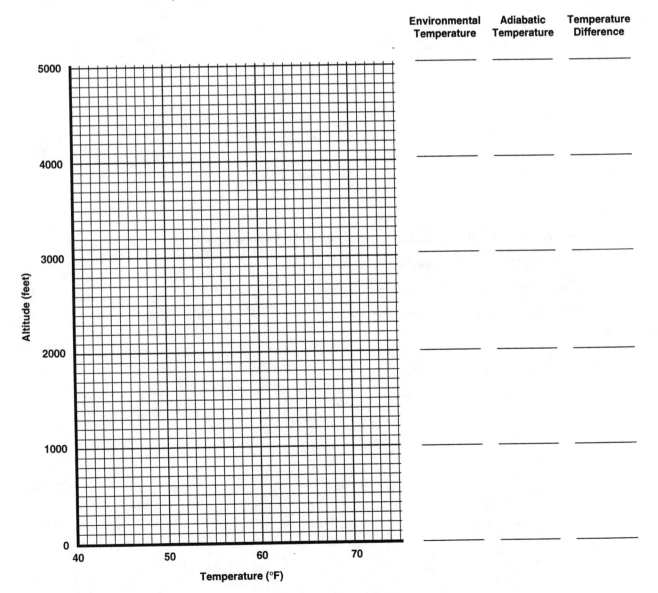

_____

9.4   An observed temperature lapse rate of 3.5°F/1000 ft is obtained. A dry-bulb reading of 45°F and a wet-bulb reading of 41°F are obtained from a parcel of air on the ground. This air is then forced up to 4000 ft. Answer the following questions about this situation. Show any necessary calculations on this page, clearly labeled.

   a.   What is the relative humidity near the ground?   _____

   b.   What is the dew point near the ground?   _____

   c.   What is the height of the LCL?   _____

   d.   Is the air stable or unstable initially?   _____

   e.   What will happen to this parcel of air if the cause of the uplift ceases after the parcel of air reaches 4000 ft?

   f.   Is precipitation likely to occur? If so, in what form?

   g.   How thick will the cloud be?   _____

9.5   A cloud base is observed to be 2200 ft above the ground. The air at ground level is 85°F.

   a.   What is the temperature at the base of the cloud?   _____

   b.   What is the dew point at ground level?   _____

   c.   What is the relative humidity near the ground?   _____

name   section   date

9.6 A parcel of air resting on the ground is 70°F, with a dew point of 43°F. An observed temperature lapse rate of 4.5°F per 1000 ft is obtained. This parcel of air is then forced to rise. Answer the following questions about this situation. Show all necessary calculations, clearly labeled. Place your answers on the lines or in the spaces provided.

a. What is the relative humidity at ground level?   _____

b. What is the height of the LCL?   _____

c. What is the temperature of the air parcel at the LCL?   _____

d. What is the proper term to express the condition of atmospheric stability or instability?   _____

e. What is the *initial* condition of stability or instability?   _____

f. At what altitude will the initial condition of stability or instability *change?* (Show your calculations for this answer.)   _____

g. What will happen to this rising parcel of air, in terms of stability, if the lifting force cannot force the air above 7000 ft?

name   section   date
_____

9.7 A parcel of air is resting on the ground. It has a temperature of 50°F and a dew point of 45.5°F. A temperature lapse rate of 7°F/1000 ft is determined. This parcel of air is then forced to rise. Answer the following
questions about this situation. Show all necessary calculations, clearly labeled. Place your answers on the
lines or in the spaces provided.

a. What is the relative humidity at ground level?   _____

b. What is the mixing ratio of this air parcel?   _____

c. What is the height of the LCL?   _____

d. Is this parcel of air stable or unstable? Explain.

e. If sublimation is assumed to begin at 30°F within this air, at what *altitude*
would this occur?   _____

f. What is the surrounding environmental temperature at the sublimation
level?   _____

g. What *form* of precipitation would most likely be reaching the ground—and why?

name   section   date

9.8 The following cross-sectional view of an island mountain range shows wind direction arrows and the location of village A and village B. Moist maritime air is forced to rise from sea level at village A to the mountain summit of 8400 ft. The air then descends to village B on the sea-level coastal plain on the leeward side of the mountain range. The air coming off the ocean to village A is 84°F with a dew point of 61.5°F.

Answer the following questions about this situation. Show all calculations in a logical sequence in the space below. Label each step in your calculations and then place your answers on the lines provided.

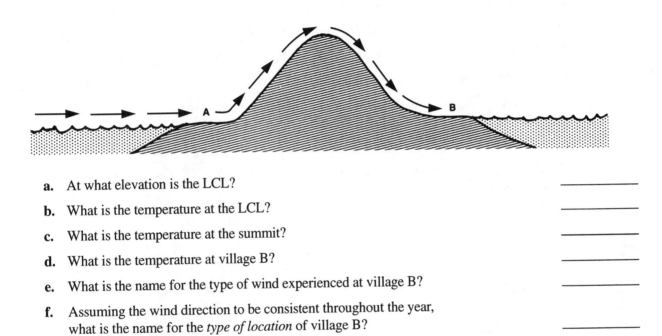

a. At what elevation is the LCL?   _____

b. What is the temperature at the LCL?   _____

c. What is the temperature at the summit?   _____

d. What is the temperature at village B?   _____

e. What is the name for the type of wind experienced at village B?   _____

f. Assuming the wind direction to be consistent throughout the year,
what is the name for the *type of location* of village B?   _____

9.9 Air rises from a plateau that is 2000 ft above sea level. This air rises upslope and over a mountain range whose summit is 9600 ft above sea level. The air then descends the leeward side of the mountain range onto another plateau that is 3000 ft above sea level. The air on the windward plateau is 70°F with a dew point of 51°F (the relative humidity is 51%).

Answer the following questions about this situation. Show all calculations in a logical sequence in the space below. Label each step in your calculations and then place your answers on the lines provided.

a. At what altitude above sea level is the LCL?   _____

b. What is the temperature of the air that was lifted to the LCL?   _____

c. What is the temperature of the air at the summit elevation of 9600 ft?   _____

d. What is the temperature on the leeward plateau?   _____

e. How much water vapor was in the air to begin with (the mixing ratio of
    the air on the plateau at 2000 ft above sea level)?   _____

f. How much water vapor should be in the air at the summit (the mixing ratio)?   _____

g. What do you think the relative humidity should be on the 3000-ft leeward plateau?
    (Calculate the answer.)   _____

name   section   date

Review and Study Questions

1. What is the general relationship between the temperature of a parcel of air and the air parcels stability?

2. What is the general consequence of atmospheric *instability* on our daily weather?

3. What are the general consequences of a *stable* atmosphere on our daily weather?

4. What are the general consequences of *conditional instability* of the atmosphere on our daily weather?

5. What factors or processes can cause the forced uplift of air and thus increase the air's instability?

6.   What factors or processes can increase the stability of the air?

7.   In what way would you expect lapse rates near the ground to vary during a day (the diurnal cycle)?

8.   Explain how the appearance of smokestack plumes are a sign of atmospheric stability conditions and describe the effects of these conditions on the distribution of pollutants.

9.   Describe the *foehn* (or chinook) wind and explain why it occurs.

10. Explain what is meant by the *adiabatic* process.

11. Why is the moist adiabatic lapse rate lower than the dry adiabatic lapse rate?

chapter 10

AIR MASSES, FRONTS, and SEVERE STORMS

An **air mass** is a large body of air that is reasonably homogenous or uniform in such properties as temperature, humidity, pressure, cloudiness, and wind flow. Air masses are usually large, covering several hundred-thousand square miles of the earth's surface with a vertical extent of several thousand feet. There are significant differences within an air mass because of its great size, such as cooler temperatures in the poleward portion. However, the general uniformity of overall temperatures, compared to the surrounding air, is what may distinguish the body of air as a recognizable air mass. Winds are seldom uniform over an area the size of an air mass, but the general air-flow pattern may show a consistency. A cold, dry, high-pressure air mass may show the clockwise and outward wind flow of the Northern Hemisphere anticyclone or it may show a strong north-wind pattern typical of a "norther." The water vapor content, as indicated by the temperature–dew-point spread and the cloud-coverage pattern, is often rather uniform within an air mass.

Air masses derive their initial properties and characteristics from their *source regions*. They also receive their names from their source regions. Thus, an Arctic (A) air mass is formed in the Arctic regions and has extremely low temperatures and, normally, very little water vapor. It should be remembered that there may be a considerable temperature contrast between continental land masses and the oceans in the middle latitudes. This temperature contrast, especially pronounced during the seasonal extremes of summer and winter, further modifies the nature of some air masses. A maritime polar (mP) air mass, noted for the low temperatures of its subpolar source region, may be significantly milder than the continental air temperatures nearby. This is due to the fact that water is warmer than land in the winter in the middle latitudes. Furthermore, in the summer the maritime polar (mP) air masses may be colder than the continental polar (cP) air masses because of the higher temperatures of land masses than of water bodies in the summer season.

Recognizing the existence of an air mass and understanding its composition go a long way toward explaining the current weather and the nature of its probable changes. A large air mass centered on an area will certainly dominate the weather of that area. A different kind of air mass about to move into a region will certainly bring with it some significant changes in weather conditions.

Air masses undergo important changes as they move away from their source regions and into and over different surface areas. Initially, they bring with them the weather of their source region. As they travel they undergo modifications according to the contrast between their internal properties and the properties of the surface over which they are moving. How slowly or rapidly an air mass moves also influences how much modification it will undergo.

A **front** is a boundary between two air masses across which significant changes in weather conditions are to be expected. When an air mass moves away from its source region it often comes into contact with another air mass and the boundary of contact between them is in the front. The front may show a separation of the air masses or it may show a clash of the air masses, depending upon the movement of each. Sharp contrasts may occur *across* the front, but relative uniformity exists *along* the front of each side. The relative uniformity of air temperatures, dew points, wind flow, and air pressures of one air mass give way to a significantly different set of conditions across the front of the adjacent air mass. These differences are experienced as changes in the weather as the air masses and their frontal boundaries move from one region toward another.

When the contrast in properties between two air masses is large, the front is sharply defined and the weather change is usually abrupt. When the contrast between two air masses is weak or gradual, the front is weak and less clearly defined and the weather changes may be gradual and less noticeable. A weak front may be a rather broad and diffuse **zone of transition** rather than a sharp boundary line.

Fronts are of great importance because of the types of weather that are associated with them. A particular sequence of weather develops with the approach and passage of the front, as well as with the formation and dissipation of a front. With an understanding of weather fronts, such sequences may be recognized and anticipated (forecast). Furthermore, the development of low pressure cells, often in sequence, occurs along a front. These cells may develop into mature cyclonic storms. Such cyclones may intensify and persist long after the initial frontal boundary dissolves and disappears.

Fronts and air masses are three-dimensional. They have length, width, and height. Weather maps show only the length of the front on the earth's surface. A **ground front** simply refers to that dimension of any type of front that lies on the earth's surface. For the front to exist as a boundary, it cannot have much width, even if it is a weak zone of transition rather than a sharp line. As a result, fronts are drawn on weather maps as lines without significant width. Just as air masses extend vertically into the atmosphere, the frontal boundary between them may exist for some distance above the surface. That part of a front that extends above the surface is referred to as the **frontal surface** or **frontal slope** to differentiate it from the ground front. A front may leave the ground and be found only in the air above the surface. Such fronts are called **upper-air fronts** or **fronts aloft.**

There are four major types of fronts. A **warm front** is a boundary between two air masses, the warmer of which is advancing. Its passage brings increasing temperatures from the warm sector behind the advancing front. The warmer air frequently contains more water vapor than the cooler air ahead of the front, so its passage will often bring an increase in humidity and cloud cover along with the rise in tem-

perature. The advancing warm air rises above the cooler air ahead of the front. As it rises, the air cools to its dew point, condensation occurs, clouds form, and precipitation develops. The clouds form in a sequence, at different distances ahead of the ground front, and may extend as much as a thousand miles out ahead of the warm front. The area of precipitation may extend for hundreds of miles. Just how far it extends depends on the slope of the front and the amount of moisture in the warm air mass.

The **cold front** boundary separates two air masses, the colder of which is advancing. Its passage brings lower temperatures and, usually, much drier air and clearing skies. As the cold air advances, it may push the less-dense, warmer, and more-moist air upwards. As this air rises and expands, it cools, condensation occurs, and a cloud forms. These vertical clouds may grow to considerable heights if the air is unstable, producing the towering cumulonimbus (thunderhead) cloud. Such clouds tend to produce very heavy rainfall with large raindrops, thunder, lightning, and sometimes hailstones. Because the cold front's slope is much steeper than that of a warm front, the uplift of air is more rapid. However, both the cloud and precipitation belts along the cold front are much narrower than those along a warm front. Frequently, the cold front will trigger a series of thunderstorm cells all along the front. The pressure exerted by the advancing cold front, and the induced pressure created by the cool downdrafts of the frontal thunderstorms themselves, sometimes create another line of thunderstorm cells in the warm air out ahead of the cold front. Such a line of convective uplift and thunderstorms is called a **squall line.** Squall-line thunderstorms are often very severe. Considerable lightning, gale-force winds, and torrential downpours accompany them. Along the squall line, which is out ahead of the cold front, a miniature cold front called a **gust front** may form. This is the result of the cool downdrafts of mature thunderstorms along the squall line, which spread out near the surface, inducing the miniature cold front between the warm air and the cool downdrafts. In many cases, the passage of a gust front (or squall line) is only a temporary reprieve. The main cold front is not far behind.

A **stationary front** is a boundary between two air masses, neither of which is advancing. Since neither air mass is advancing, the contrast in the properties of the adjacent air masses must still be sufficient for the front to exist. It follows that if any type of front becomes stationary and remains stationary long enough, the contrasts between the adjacent air masses will diminish and the frontal boundary must eventually dissolve. A stationary front may eventually begin to advance in a certain direction, however. As this occurs, the front will become either a warm front or a cold front, depending on which air mass is advancing. Warm fronts that become stationary fronts tend to maintain the characteristics of the original warm front. Cold fronts that become stationary fronts tend to take on the characteristics of a warm front as a result of the reduction in the steepness of the frontal surface. The steepness of the frontal surface depends upon the length of time a front remains stationary, the wind and pressure differences along the front, and the upper-air conditions. Stationary fronts are common breeding areas for the development of low pressure cells that develop into cyclones. In tropical latitudes, these frontal disturbances may lead to the development of cyclones that eventually mature into full-fledged hurricanes.

The **occluded front** results from the advancement of a given front to the point at which it has caught up with a part of another front. Because a front is simply a boundary between two air masses, it follows that two or more fronts may exist when there are three or more air masses in a region. When one front, such as a cold front, catches up with part of a warm front, the parts that merge produce the occlusion. Cold fronts advance more rapidly, on the average, than warm fronts, so it is usually the cold front that catches up with and occludes the warm front. Such occlusions may produce either **warm-front occlusions** or **cold-front occlusions,** depending upon which of the original fronts remains on the ground and which is lifted off the ground by the occlusion. This depends upon the temperature and density of the air masses involved. If the air behind an original cold front is colder and denser than the air that was ahead of the original warm front, then the cold front will remain on the ground during the occlusion and it will be a cold-front

occlusion. The warm front, lifted off the ground, will become an **upper-air warm front** (a warm front aloft). Sometimes the air *ahead* of the warm front is colder and denser than the air behind a cold front. In this situation, the occlusion will result in the cold front lifting off the ground to produce an **upper-air cold front** (a cold front aloft) and the warm front will stay on the ground. The occlusion, in this case, is a **warm-front occlusion.** Upper-air fronts, still serving as boundaries between different air masses in the upper air, are of great significance in aviation meteorology.

The process of frontal formation, called **frontogenesis,** results primarily from a pressure distribution that allows the wind to move air of contrasting temperatures and moisture content into a zone of conflict. Conditions of pressure and wind flow conducive to the formation of fronts are known as **deformation fields.** It is here that a front may be born.

The process of dissipation of a front, in which the contrast between the adjacent air masses disappears and the front dies, is called **frontolysis.** The process of occlusion is, therefore, a process of frontolysis. An occlusion usually marks the eventual disappearance of the contrast between air masses as a result of mixing and blending. The air masses that occlude, such as a cold air mass and a cool air mass, have less contrast than existed between the original air masses on either side of the original cold front and the original warm front. It should be remembered that when a cold *front* and a warm *front* occlude, it is the cold air *behind* the cold front that is mixing with the cold air *ahead* of the warm front. The diminution of the contrast between adjacent air masses separated by a stationary front will also result in dissipation of the stationary front if the front remains stationary for long.

The search of plotted weather data to discover the location and types of weather fronts, and to predict future weather conditions based upon projected changes in the movements and contrasts of fronts, is called **frontal analysis.** Frontal analysis is treated in Chapter 12, Weather Analysis and Forecasting.

name   section   date

Exercises

AIR MASSES AND FRONTS

10.1 Complete the following chart by listing the *names* of the six major types of air masses, the standard weather map *abbreviations* for each, and the general *temperature-humidity* characteristics (distinguishing summer-winter differences when necessary) for each air mass.

Air mass name	Abbreviation	Temperature-humidity characteristics

10.2 Complete the following chart by listing the *names* of the four major types of ground fronts and by adding the proper *symbols* for each type of front on the frontal lines provided.

Name of weather front	Weather map symbol
	————————————————
	————————————————
	————————————————
	————————————————

10.3 The following deformation field diagram shows the locations of two high-pressure cells and two low-pressure cells—all in the Northern Hemisphere.

   a. Draw numerous short arrows to show the wind-flow pattern.

   b. Draw a heavy dark line to show where *frontogenesis* should occur.

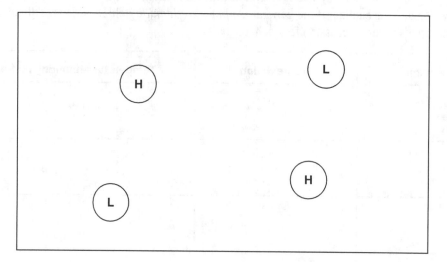

10.4 The map below shows a cold front and a warm front. The cold front is advancing 600 mi per day (1.5 in. on the map) while the warm front is advancing 400 mi per day (1 in. on the map). *Redraw the fronts* to show their positions one day from the present situation; include any new front that may be needed.

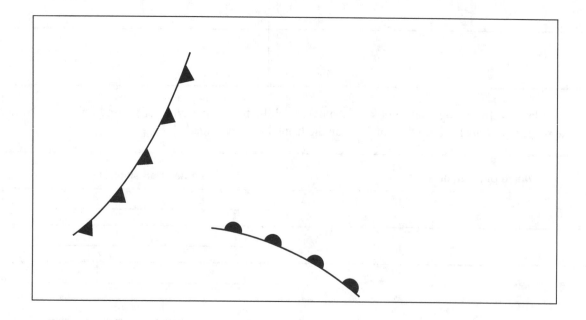

name   section   date

10.5 In the following boxes draw the *frontal slopes* of typical weather fronts as required. These are to be vertical (cross-sectional) views of the frontal surfaces from the ground up into the lower troposphere.

a. A cold front

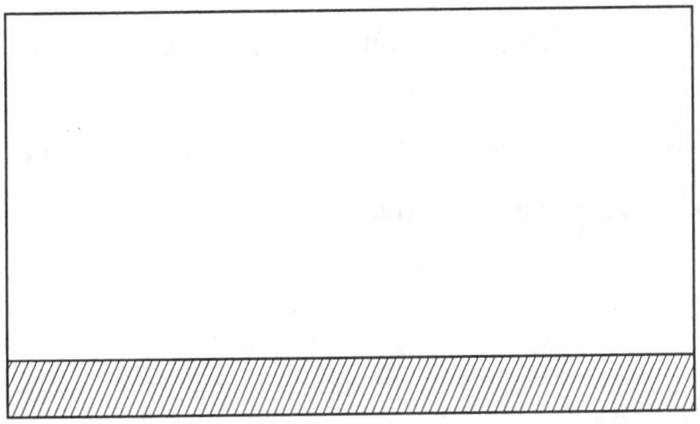

b. A warm front

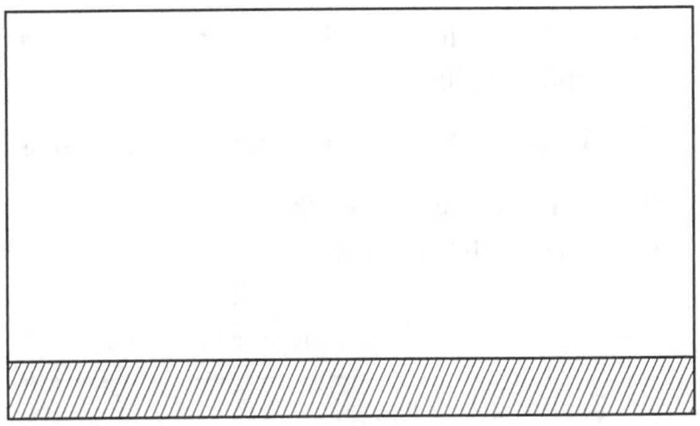

c. A former cold front that is now a stationary front

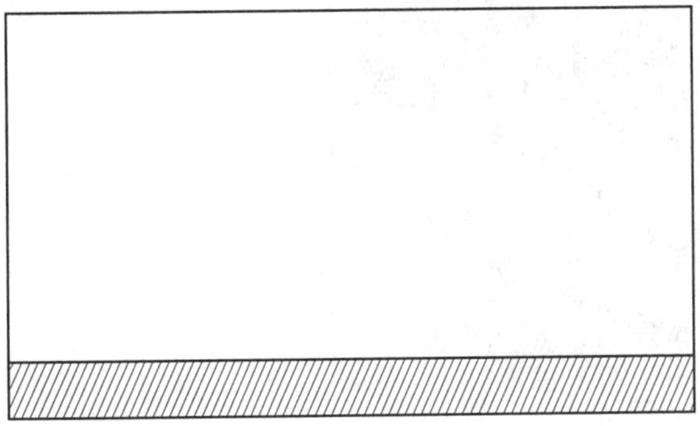

d. An occluded front at the first moment of the occlusion

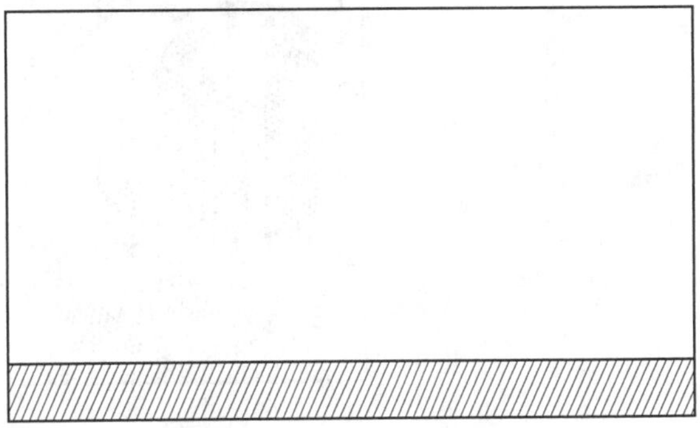

e. A warm-front occlusion

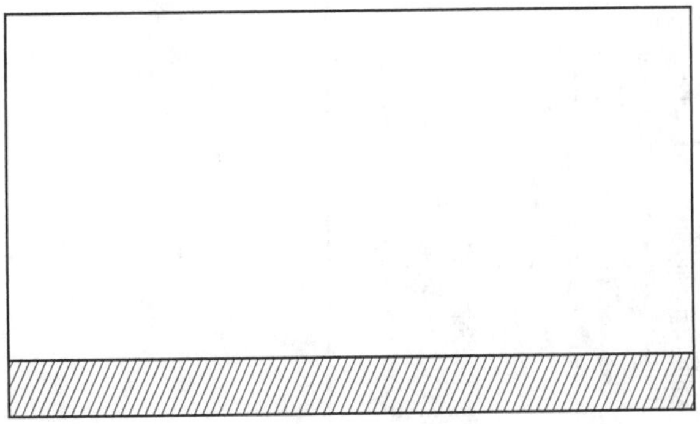

f. A cold-front occlusion

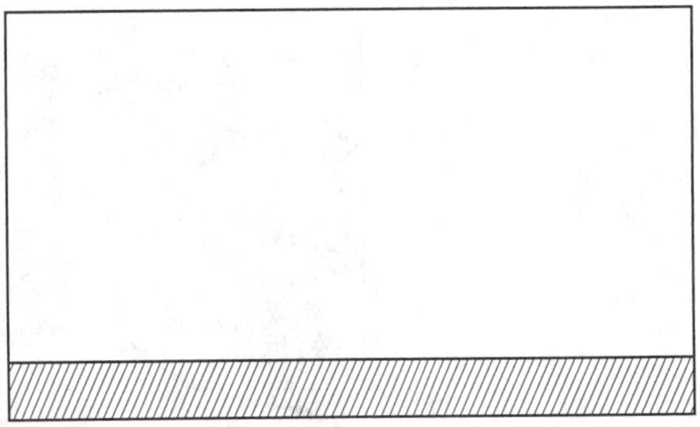

name   section   date
_____

10.6 The two maps below show the average location of major North American air masses. The shaded areas indicate those air masses and their source regions. The heavy lines suggest their typical boundary positions. The white regions found between air masses represent the major regions of conflict among the air masses. You are to do the following:

a. Label each of the six major summer air masses of North America with its proper symbol (weather map abbreviation).

b. Label each of the six major winter air masses of North America with its proper abbreviation symbol.

c. What would you expect to find in the white areas (the regions of conflict among the air masses)? _____

Summer air mass

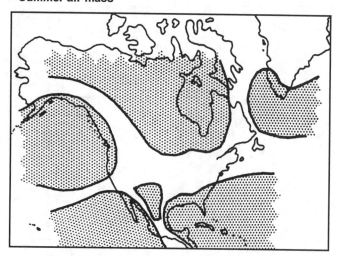

Winter air mass

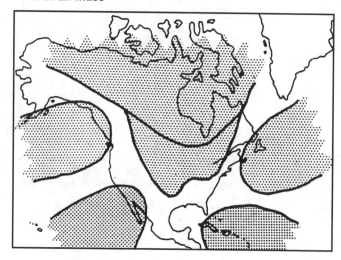

name   section   date

STORMS

10.7 Water vapor sublimates and tiny cloud droplets freeze into very tiny ice crystals in the high portions of a cumulonimbus (thunderhead) cloud. These ice crystals keep growing, as they fall through the cloud, to produce snowflakes. If the lower portion of the cloud (and the air beneath the cloud base) is warm enough, the snowflakes will melt into raindrops.

    a. Using Diagram A below, show the regions within the cloud that would be expected to contain:

        1. Primarily ice crystals (use small checks: ✓✓✓)

        2. Primarily snowflakes (use snow symbol: ✳✳✳✳)

        3. Primarily raindrops (use rain symbol: ∴∴•)

    b. Using Diagram B, *repeat* the above procedure of labeling the regions of the cloud, but note the temperature profile is quite different this time.

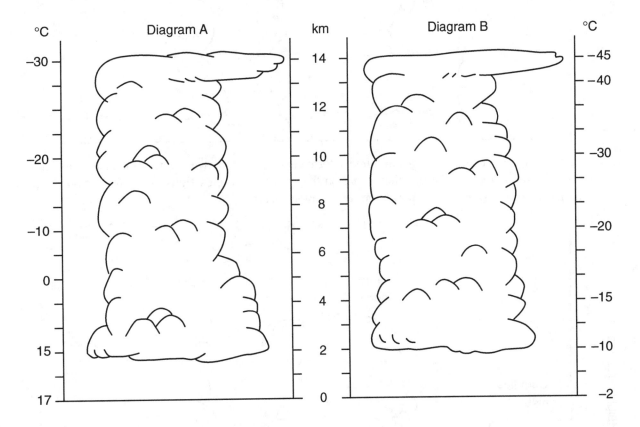

    c. If in Diagram B the ground-level temperature was 3°C and the temperature at the 2-km level was 0°C, what might be the form of precipitation reaching the ground? Why?

name   section   date

10.8 For each of the three major stages in the development of a thunderstorm shown below, indicate the general pattern of updrafts or downdrafts—or both—by sketching in as many *short arrows* as necessary to clearly show the pattern of air flow within the clouds.

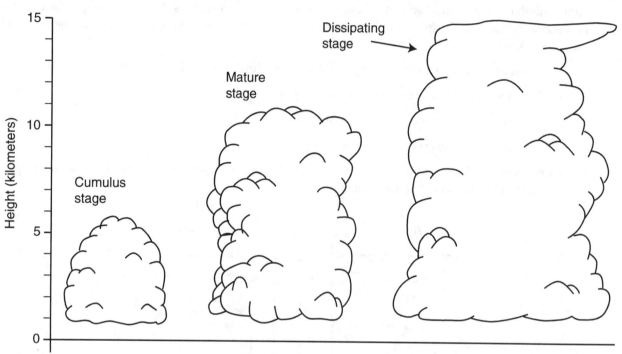

10.9 For each of the three major stages of thunderstorm development shown below, indicate the general pattern of *electrical charges* within the clouds and on the ground. Use plus signs (+++) for regions of positive charge and minus signs (– – –) for regions of negative charge.

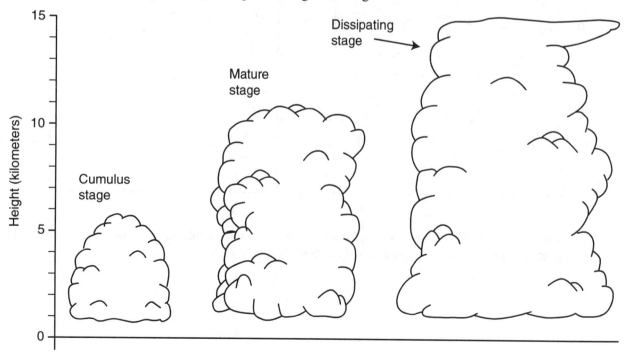

name   section   date

10.10 Most textbooks provide several maps or tables which depict the frequency patterns for various types of severe storms and related phenomena in the United States. Using such maps and tables, answer the following questions:

a.   Where are the areas that have the highest annual number of days with thunderstorms?

b.   Where are the areas that have the greatest frequency of tornadoes?

c.   Where are the areas that have the greatest frequency of days with hail?

d.   Where are the regions with the highest frequency of hurricane "landfalls"?

name   section   date
_____

10.11 If your textbook provides any map or table information on the frequency of severe storms on a *global* basis, then indicate the major regions outside of the United States with high frequencies of the following:

   a. Thunderstorms (lightning, hail)

   b. Tornadoes

   c. Hurricanes

10.12 Briefly describe other types of severe weather that are not necessarily associated with storms.

name   section   date

HURRICANE TRACKING: HURRICANES CAMILLE AND CAROL

10.13 Data for two very interesting hurricanes (Camille in 1969 and Carol in 1954) are given on the following page.

a. Using the data in Table 10.1 and the hurricane tracking chart following the data (extra charts may be found in Appendix B), plot the positions of Hurricane Camille as follows:

1. Plot Camille's position at 0000 GMT (7:00 P.M. EST) using the open circle (○). Plot Camille's position at 1200 GMT (7:00 A.M. EST) using a solid circle (●). *Label* each position by *date.* (You may want to read the section in Chapter 11 on time on weather maps and charts.) Note: 0000 GMT on any date is actually 7:00 P.M. *the day before,* in EST!

2. Connect the positions of Camille, from the above plotting, by using the following standard symbols:

•••••••••••••••• Tropical depression: Winds less than 34 KT (39 MPH).
------------------ Tropical storm: Winds 34 KT (39 MPH) or more but less than 64 KT (74 MPH).
——————— Hurricane: Winds 64 KT (74 MPH) and above.
*********** Depression (dissipation stage): Winds once again less than 34 KT (39 MPH).

Because the storm's wind speed may have passed one of the above critical values at 0600 GMT or 1800 GMT (between the two hours each day you have plotted), you should examine the raw data to determine if there were any *changes* in the storm's *status* (depression, tropical storm, hurricane) *between* the 12-hr periods plotted. If such a change occurred between the hours plotted, the symbol should reflect this change. Thus, if the storm was a tropical storm at 0000 GMT and a hurricane at 1200 GMT, you should look at the data for 0600 GMT that day to see whether or not the hurricane wind speed was reached by 0600 GMT. If it was reached by 0600, then the plotting symbol should show this as follows: -----○----——●→

b. Follow the above directions and repeat the plotting process for the data on Hurricane *Carol.* Use the *same* hurricane tracking chart you used for Camille so you will be able to *compare* the tracks of the two hurricanes.

c. Based on both the original data in Table 10.1 and the tracking chart you just prepared answer the following questions.

1. How many *consecutive* hours was each storm able to sustain hurricane force?
Carol _____   Camille _____

2. How many hours was each storm able to maintain hurricane force while moving over *land?*
Carol _____   Camille _____

3. What was the *shortest distance* traveled during any given 24-hr period?
(Give the answer in both degrees and miles. One degree of latitude is approximately 69 mi.)
Carol _____   Camille _____

4. Why do these storms change direction eastward between 30 degrees and 35 degrees N?

name   section   date

TABLE 10.1   Hurricanes Camille and Carol

	Camille, August 1969					Carol, August 1954			
Day	Time (GMT)	Position Lat.	Long.	Wind (MPH)	Day	Time (GMT)	Position Lat.	Long.	Wind (MPH)
14	1800	19.4	82.0	58	25	1200	24.0	74.9	35
15	0000	19.7	82.7	63		1800	25.1	75.5	46
	0600	20.1	83.3	69	26	0000	26.1	76.0	52
	1200	20.7	83.8	98		0600	27.0	76.3	63
	1800	21.2	84.1	115		1200	27.7	76.4	69
16	0000	22.3	84.4	104		1800	28.4	76.3	69
	0600	23.1	85.2	121	27	0000	28.9	76.2	81
	1200	23.7	85.9	138		0600	29.3	76.3	86
	1800	24.2	86.5	150		1200	29.6	76.5	92
17	0000	25.2	87.2	161		1800	29.8	76.6	98
	0600	26.0	87.7	178	28	0000	29.9	76.7	98
	1200	27.0	88.2	184		0600	30.1	76.9	98
	1800	28.3	88.7	190		1200	30.3	77.2	98
18	0000	29.4	89.1	190		1800	30.4	77.4	98
	0600	30.7	89.6	115	29	0000	30.5	77.6	98
	1200	32.2	90.0	75		0600	30.7	77.8	92
	1800	33.4	90.1	58		1200	30.9	77.9	92
19	0000	34.7	90.0	35		1800	31.2	78.0	92
	0600	36.0	89.3	35	30	0000	31.5	78.1	92
	1200	37.0	88.0	35		0600	31.9	78.0	98
	1800	37.7	86.0	29		1200	32.5	77.6	98
20	0000	38.0	84.8	29		1800	33.1	77.0	98
	0600	37.4	80.2	29	31	0000	34.2	76.1	98
	1200	37.3	77.0	29		0600	37.3	74.2	98
	1800	37.0	75.1	35		1200	40.2	72.9	98
21	0000	36.6	73.4	46		1800	43.1	71.8	86
	0600	36.7	70.9	52	9/1	0000	46.2	71.1	69
	1200	37.3	68.4	58		0600	48.9	71.2	58
	1800	38.0	64.9	63					
22	0000	39.2	61.4	69					
	0600	40.8	58.2	48					
	1200	43.0	54.0	43					

name   section   date

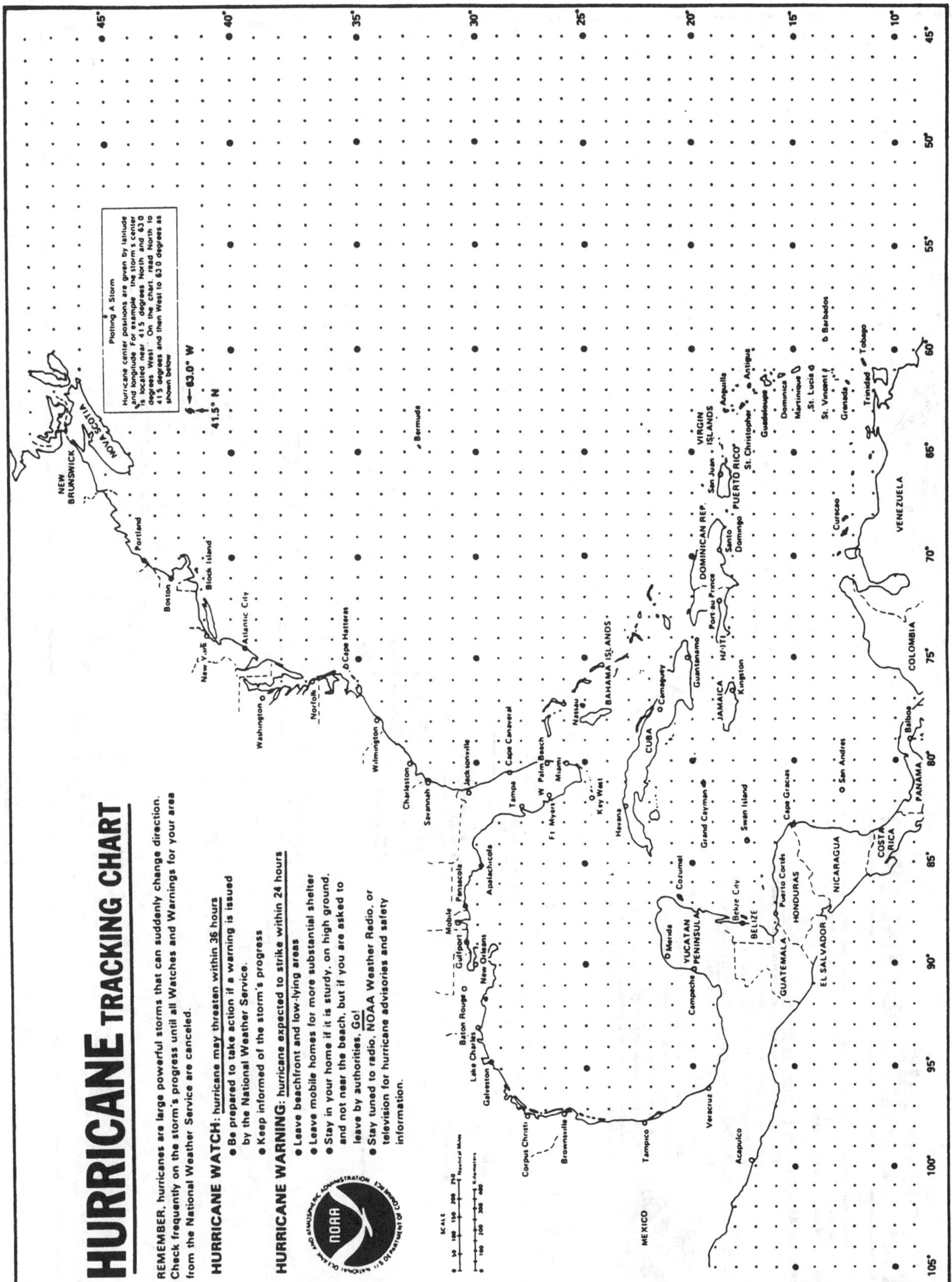

Map 10. 1   Hurricane tracking chart.

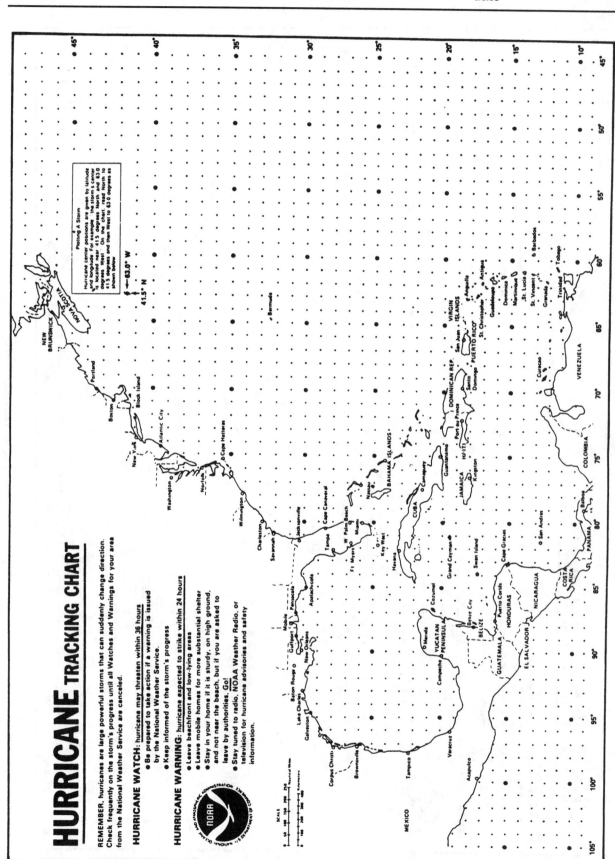

Map 10. 2   Hurricane tracking chart.

name   section   date

HURRICANE TRACKING: HURRICANES INIKI AND GEORGETTE

10.14 Data for two recent Pacific hurricanes (Iniki and Georgette, both in 1992) are given in Table 10.2 on page 155.

a. Using the data in Table 10.2 and the hurricane tracking chart following the data (extra charts may be found in Appendix B), plot the positions of Hurricane Iniki as follows:

   1. Plot Iniki's position at 0000 GMT (4:00 P.M. Pacific Time) using an open circle (○). Plot Iniki's position at 1200 GMT (4:00 A.M. Pacific Time) using a solid circle (●). *Label* each position by *date.* (You may want to read the section in Chapter 11 on *time* on weather maps and charts.) Note: 0000 GMT on any date is actually 4:00 P.M. *the day before;* in Pacific Time (7:00 P.M. *the day before,* in eastern standard time)! And, 0600 GMT is 10:00 P.M. the day before, in Pacific Time (1:00 A.M. that day in eastern standard time). (NOTE: You should *ignore* the map *insert* of the Hawaiian Islands and *extend the grid* of the base map as necessary.)

   2. Connect the positions of Iniki, from the above plotting, by using the following standard symbols:

   •••••••••••••••• Tropical depression: Winds less than 34 KT (39 MPH).
   ------------------ Tropical storm: Winds 34 KT (39 MPH) or more but less than 64 KT (74 MPH).
   ———————— Hurricane: Winds 64 KT (74 MPH) and above.
   ************ Depression (dissipation stage): Winds once again less than 34 KT (39 MPH).

   Because the storm's wind speed may have passed one of the above critical values at 0600 GMT or 1800 GMT (between the two hours each day you will plot), you should examine the raw data to determine if there were any *changes* in the storm's *status* (depression, tropical storm, hurricane) *between* the 12-hr period plotted. If such a change occurred between the hours plotted, the symbol should reflect this change. Thus, if the storm was a tropical storm at 0000 GMT and a hurricane at 1200 GMT, you should look at the data for 0600 that day to see whether or not hurricane wind speed was reached by 0600. If it was reached by 0600 or 1800 hours, then the plotting symbol should show this as follows: -----○---———●→

b. Follow the above directions and repeat the plotting process for the data on Hurricane Georgette. Use the same tracking chart you used for Iniki so you will be able to *compare* the tracks of the two hurricanes.

c. Based on both the original data in Table 10.2 and the tracking chart you just prepared answer the following questions.

   1. How many consecutive *days* was each storm able to sustain hurricane force?

   Iniki_____ Georgette_____

   2. Which storm maintained hurricane force longer?   _____

   3. Which storm traveled farthest (as a hurricane)?   _____

   4. Which hurricane was more uniform in speed?   _____

   5. What was the maximum wind speed, in both knots and miles per hour for:

   Iniki: knots _____   MPH_____

   Georgette: knots _____   MPH_____

   6. What was the lowest pressure for:

   Iniki _____ Georgette_____

name   section   date
_____

7. Which hurricane appears to have weakened only to intensify again before finally weakening? _____ What evidence do you have for this (use dates and times)?

8. What relationship appears to exist between pressure and wind speed? (Give specific evidence.)

name   section   date

TABLE 10.2   Hurricanes Iniki and Georgette

		Hurricane Iniki, September 1992							Hurricane Georgette, July 1992				
Day	Time (GMT)	Position Lat.	Long.	Pressure (mb)	Wind (kt)	Speed (MPH)	Day	Time (GMT)	Position Lat.	Long.	Pressure (mb)	Wind (kt)	Speed (MPH)
5	0600	11.7	131.5	1010	25		14	1200	10.8	94.2	1011	25	
	1200	11.7	133.0	1009	25			1800	11.3	95.3	1010	30	
	1800	11.7	134.5	1008	30		15	0000	11.8	96.4	1009	30	
6	0000	11.6	135.9	1008	30			0600	12.2	97.4	1005	35	
	0600	11.6	137.1	1008	30			1200	12.5	98.3	1000	45	
	1200	11.6	138.3	1007	30			1800	12.7	99.2	994	55	
	1800	11.4	139.2	1006	30		16	0000	12.8	100.1	988	65	
7	0000	11.2	140.0	1005	30			0600	13.0	101.0	984	65	
	0600	11.3	140.9	1005	30			1200	13.1	102.0	981	70	
	1200	11.6	142.0	1005	30			1800	13.2	103.0	978	75	
	1800	11.7	143.2	1004	30		17	0000	13.4	104.0	975	80	
8	0000	11.7	144.5	1002	35			0600	13.8	105.0	972	85	
	0600	12.0	146.0	1000	40			1200	14.2	106.0	970	90	
	1200	12.1	147.5	1000	40			1800	14.8	107.0	968	95	
	1800	12.3	149.0	996	50		18	0000	15.4	108.0	965	95	
9	0000	12.4	150.2	996	60			0600	16.0	109.2	964	95	
	0600	12.7	151.6	992	65			1200	16.7	110.4	965	95	
	1200	13.0	152.9	992	65			1800	17.3	111.6	968	95	
	1800	13.4	154.3	984	80		19	0000	17.7	112.7	970	90	
10	0000	13.8	155.5	980	85			0600	18.0	113.7	973	85	
	0600	14.3	156.9	960	90			1200	18.4	114.6	976	80	
	1200	14.7	157.8	960	100			1800	18.5	115.3	979	80	
	1800	15.2	158.6	951	100		20	0000	18.5	116.0	981	75	
11	0000	15.9	159.3	948	110			0600	18.4	116.7	982	75	
	0600	16.8	159.8	947	115			1200	18.1	117.4	980	75	
	1200	18.2	160.2	939	120			1800	17.9	118.0	976	80	
	1800	19.5	160.0	938	125		21	0000	17.7	118.7	972	85	
12	0000	21.5	159.8	945	115			0600	17.5	119.5	970	90	
	0600	23.7	159.4	959	100			1200	17.5	120.5	968	95	
	1200	25.7	159.0	980	80			1800	17.6	121.7	970	90	
	1800	28.1	158.9	980	80		22	0000	17.7	123.1	974	85	
13	0000	30.4	158.8	990	65			0600	17.8	124.6	978	75	
	0600	33.0	158.7	990	65			1200	17.9	126.2	984	70	
	1200	35.0	158.5	1000	50			1800	17.9	127.8	989	65	
	1800	36.7	158.1	1002	40		23	0000	17.8	129.5	994	55	
								0600	17.7	131.4	997	50	
								1200	17.5	133.4	999	45	
								1800	17.5	135.4	1002	40	
							24	0000	17.5	137.4	1005	35	
								0600	17.5	139.4	1007	30	
								1200	17.6	141.5	1008	30	
								1800	17.8	143.5	1009	30	
							25	0000	17.9	145.0	1010	25	
								0600	17.8	147.4	1010	25	
								1200	17.8	149.5	1011	25	
								1800	17.8	151.7	1011	25	
							26	0000	17.5	154.0	1012	30	
								0600	17.3	156.2	1013	30	
								1200	17.0	158.4	1015	30	
								1800	16.6	160.1	1016	25	
							27	0000	16.3	162.5	1017	25	
								0600	16.3	164.5	1017	25	
								1200	16.1	166.5	1017	25	
								1800	16.0	169.0	1017	25	

name section date

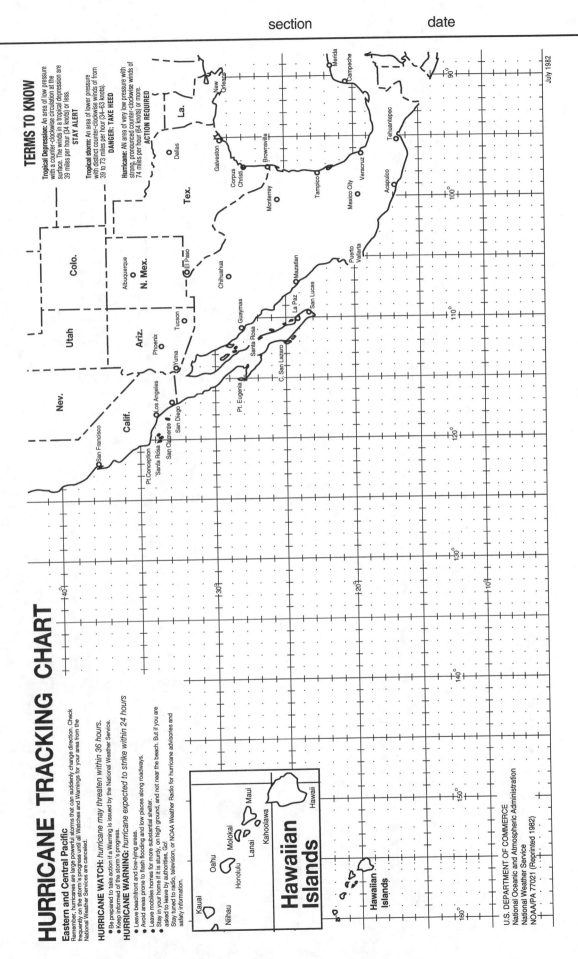

HURRICANE TRACKING CHART

Eastern and Central Pacific
Remember, hurricanes are large powerful storms that can suddenly change direction. Check frequently on the storm's progress until all Watches and Warnings for your area from the National Weather Services are canceled.

HURRICANE WATCH: *hurricane may threaten within 36 hours.*
● Be prepared to take action if a Warning is issued by the National Weather Service.
● Keep informed of the storm's progress.
HURRICANE WARNING: *hurricane expected to strike within 24 hours*
● Leave beachfront and low-lying areas.
● Avoid areas prone to flash flooding and low places along roadways.
● Leave mobiles homes for more substantial shelter.
● Stay in your home if it is sturdy, on high ground, and not near the beach. But if you are asked to leave by authorities, Go!
● Stay tuned to radio, television, or NOAA Weather Radio for hurricane advisories and safety information.

TERMS TO KNOW

Tropical Depression: An area of low pressure with a counter-clockwise circulation at the surface. The winds in a tropical depression are 39 miles per hour (34 knots) or less.
STAY ALERT

Tropical storm: An area of lower pressure with distinct counter-clockwise winds of from 39 to 73 miles per hour (34–63 knots).
DANGER: TAKE HEED

Hurricane: AN area of very low pressure with strong, pronounced counter-clockwise winds of 74 miles per hour (64 knots) or more.
ACTION REQUIRED

July 1982

Hawaiian Islands

Kauai
Niihau
Oahu
Honolulu
Molokai
Lanai
Maui
Kahoolawa
Hawaii

Hawaiian Islands

U.S. DEPARTMENT OF COMMERCE
National Oceanic and Atmospheric Administration
National Weather Service
NOAA/PA 77021 (Reprinted 1982)

Map 10.3 Hurricane tracking chart.

name   section   date

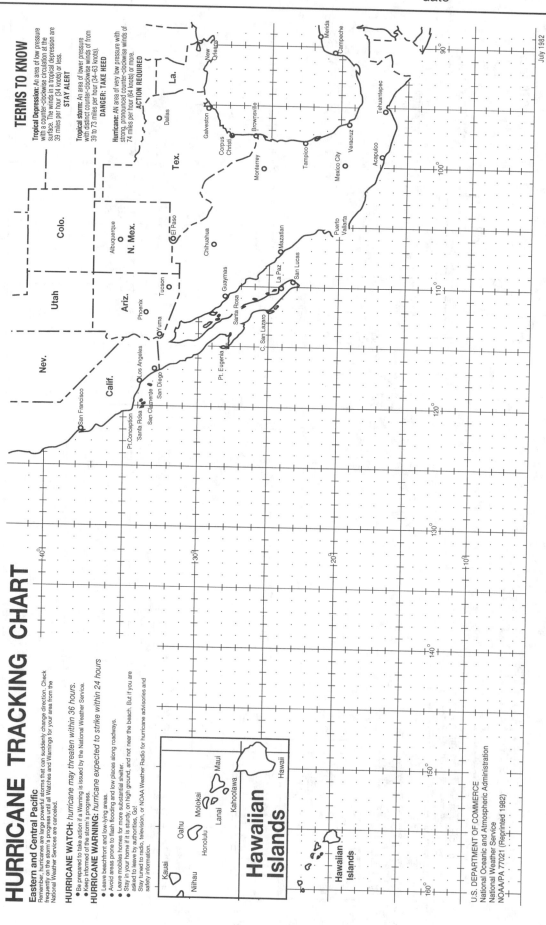

HURRICANE TRACKING CHART

Eastern and Central Pacific

Remember, hurricanes are large powerful storms that can suddenly change direction. Check frequently on the storm's progress until all Watches and Warnings for your area from the National Weather Services are canceled.

HURRICANE WATCH: *hurricane may threaten within 36 hours.*
• Be prepared to take action if a Warning is issued by the National Weather Service.
• Keep informed of the storm's progress.
HURRICANE WARNING: *hurricane expected to strike within 24 hours*
• Leave beachfront and low-lying areas.
• Avoid areas prone to flash flooding and low places along roadways.
• Leave mobiles homes for more substantial shelter.
• Stay in your home if it is sturdy, on high ground, and not near the beach. But if you are asked to leave by authorities, Go!
Stay tuned to radio, television, or NOAA Weather Radio for hurricane advisories and safety information.

Hawaiian Islands

Kauai
Niihau
Oahu
Honolulu
Molokai
Lanai
Maui
Kahoolawe
Hawaii

Hawaiian Islands

TERMS TO KNOW

Tropical Depression: An area of low pressure with a counter-clockwise circulation at the surface. The winds in a tropical depression are 39 miles per hour (34 knots) or less.
STAY ALERT
Tropical storm: An area of lower pressure with distinct counter-clockwise winds of from 39 to 73 miles per hour (34–63 knots).
DANGER: TAKE HEED
Hurricane: AN area of very low pressure with strong, pronounced counter-clockwise winds of 74 miles per hour (64 knots) or more.
ACTION REQUIRED

July 1982

U.S. DEPARTMENT OF COMMERCE
National Oceanic and Atmospheric Administration
National Weather Service
NOAA/PA 77021 (Reprinted 1982)

Extra Work Map—Hurricane tracking chart.

name   section   date

Review and Study Questions

1. What are two major factors that influence the amount of *change* that takes place within an air mass?

2. Briefly describe the weather that is typical of places that are *centered* in the *middle* of each major type of air mass.

3. What determines how narrow or how wide the frontal zone of transition will be?

4. What changes in the weather take place as a result of the passage of a warm front?

5. What changes in the weather should be expected as a result of the passage of a cold front?

6. What sequence of weather occurs with the coming and passage of an occluded front?

7. Weather conditions associated with stationary fronts are similar to those associated with what other type of front?

8. What is the typical sequence of cloud types associated with a warm front (from a position ahead of the front moving towards the ground front itself)?

9. How far ahead of the warm front might the associated clouds extend?

10. What determines the steepness of the slope of a cold front?

11. Describe the clouds and type of precipitation associated with a typical cold front.

12. What determines whether an occlusion will be a cold-front type or a warm-front type?

13. What happens to the original warm air of the warm air mass in the case of a warm-front occlusion? In the case of a cold-front occlusion?

14. How is the type of weather front related to:

    a. the development of layered (stratiform) clouds versus vertical (cumuliform) clouds,

    b. drizzle versus large raindrops, and

    c. brief versus prolonged precipitation?

chapter 11

THE WEATHER MAP

The weather map is the most fundamental tool for understanding and predicting the weather. A large number of weather maps and charts are produced, at various hours of the day and in many forms, including a large number of facsimile products, both land-line and marine radiofacsimile. Facsimile products are exact reproductions of the original documents and are transmitted by wire or radio.

Weather maps received as facsimile products include numerous analysis charts, a great variety of prognostic charts, and many other charts including satellite photographs, weather depictions, wave-height charts, cloud studies, radar summaries, and sea-temperature and ice-information charts. A few of the common terms used to refer to certain types of facsimile products or other weather charts are given below.

Analysis Charts.   These are maps that show the existing conditions at a given moment. They show the pressure pattern, especially the centers of high and low pressure. They may also show the weather fronts and other observational data from each observation station. Among the charts distributed by the National Weather Service are several Surface Analysis and Upper-Air Analysis charts, Surface Pressure Change Analysis, Maximum and Minimum Temperature Chart, the Observed 24-Hour Precipitation Amounts Chart, Winds Aloft and Tropopause Chart, and Observed Snow Cover. The Surface Analysis Chart is the one generally thought of as "the weather map." There are many printed forms of this chart, including the official Daily Weather Map, and a great variety of simplified versions found in newspapers and magazines and on television weather programs.

Prognosis Charts.   These are *forecast* charts. They show the expected or forecast conditions for an area at a specified *future* time. They show the expected pressure pattern and may include additional forecast information. Prognosis charts (progs) include the surface progs for 12, 24, 26, and 48 hr., the Low-Level Significant Weather progs, Precipitation-Probability progs, Heavy-Snow Guidance Forecasts, Daily Minimum and Maximum Temperature, the Severe Weather Outlook, the Wind-Wave/Swell/Combined Sea Height Forecasts, and numerous upper-air and wind charts.

Synoptic Charts.   This is a term that refers to weather observations that are both in overall summary form and made simultaneously at many observation points. Thus, the analysis chart is essentially a synoptic chart and is frequently referred to as such.

Significant Weather Charts.   These are charts that focus on only the major weather patterns, such as frontal systems, cloud patterns, precipitation regions, and fog areas. Such charts may be either analysis (showing recent conditions) or prognosis (showing forecast conditions).

Nephanalysis Charts.   These are charts that present analysis of satellite photographs of clouds (*nepho-* indicates "clouds"). A satellite ice chart is included in this category, and some ice-edge information is commonly included on the nephanalysis chart itself.

Sea Conditions Chart.   A variety of charts, both analysis and prognosis, depict sea conditions (primarily from marine radiofacsimile). Some show the sea-surface temperatures, some show significant wave heights, and some show the limits of sea ice.

Upper-Air Charts. This is a term for a large variety of charts, both analysis and prognosis, of upper-air wind, pressure, thickness, wind shear, vorticity, and significant weather. Such upper-air charts are presented for a variety of upper air pressure surfaces (heights).

Extended Forecast Charts. These are charts that present forecasts (prognoses) three or more days in advance. Among these charts are the Extended Daily Sea Level Prognosis, Extended Daily Precipitation Prognosis, Daily Minimum and Maximum Temperature Forecasts, and Five-Day Mean Minimum and Maximum Temperature Anomalies and Quantitative Precipitation classes and the Average Monthly Weather Outlook.

The surface-analysis chart is basic to all others. It tells you present or very recent weather conditions. It also presents the symbolic language of meteorology that is the basis for understanding most other weather charts.

Time on Weather Maps and Charts

To correctly use the many available weather maps (especially facsimile charts) you should understand the time factors involved. The time given on analysis charts is the time of the observations, which is necessarily earlier than the time of transmission, receipt, or publication of the map. The time given on prognosis charts is the **valid time** (VT), which is *subsequent* to the time the chart is transmitted and received. The notation on an analysis chart might read as follows:

SFC PRES ANAL 18Z 12 DEC 96

This chart is the surface-pressure analysis chart for 1800 hr Zulu (18Z) for 12 December 1996. The time is expressed as military time, so that 18Z is 6 hr past noon, or 6:00 P.M. (The Z stands for *Zulu*, which is a communications code word. It represents an arbitrarily chosen value for *time*.) Because at a given moment different places on the earth have different times, a specific standard had to be established for Zulu. This standard is the time at the prime meridian (zero degrees

longitude), the Greenwich meridian. Therefore, Zulu means Greenwich Mean Time (GMT), also known as Universal Coordinated Time (UCT) or simply Universal Time (UT), and Greenwich Civil Time (GCT). All of these expressions refer to average solar time reckoned from midnight on the Greenwich (prime) meridian.

The time given on a particular chart must be converted to one's own time. The following table provides the necessary conversion factors. Notice the additional factor for daylight saving time.

GMT to standard time:		Standard time to GMT:		
GMT − 4 = Atlantic		Atlantic	+ 4 = GMT
GMT − 5 = Eastern		Eastern	+ 5 = GMT
GMT − 6 = Central		Central	+ 6 = GMT
GMT − 7 = Mountain		Mountain	+ 7 = GMT
GMT − 8 = Pacific		Pacific	+ 8 = GMT
GMT − 9 = Yukon		Yukon	+ 9 = GMT
GMT − 10 = Alaskan		Alaskan	+ 10 = GMT
GMT − 11 = Bering		Bering	+ 11 = GMT

Subtract one less hour for daylight saving time.	Add one less hour for daylight saving time.

Thus, 18Z (1800 GMT) to a person in the eastern standard time zone would mean 1300 hr (18 hrs minus 5 hrs) or 1:00 P.M. eastern time. However, if daylight saving time is in effect, one hour *less* should be subtracted and 18Z would mean 2:00 P.M. EDT. The notation on a prognosis chart might read as follows:

SIG WX PROG:400-150 MB
DATE: 13 JAN 96
VT: 0600Z

This chart is the significant weather prognosis (SIG WX PROG) for the 400–150-mb height. It was transmitted on January 12, 1996, but was dated January 13 (being a forecast chart). VT 0600Z means that the valid time (VT) is 0600 hr Zulu (GMT) on January 13, which is 0100 hr (1:00 A.M.) eastern standard time. When you work with a map or chart, you should note immediately the particular time to which the charted information applies—either a recent time (in analysis charts) or a valid time in the future (in prognosis charts).

Coded Weather Data and the Station Plot

Hundreds of observation points, both land stations and ships, provide a great variety and quantity of weather data. Each station observes and transmits certain basic information, while special classes of stations may collect and transmit additional data. The information gathered at a land station (and eventually plotted on a map) is different from that gathered aboard a ship. The type and amount of information and the time of observation differ among the various classes of weather stations. Most of these differences are not critical to a basic understanding of the map.

Some weather information, particularly that which is numerical, is quite simple in concept and in form of presentation. Other pieces of weather information require more elaborate presentation. While only a number is needed to convey the temperature, there are 100 possible symbols available to describe the present weather. The number of symbols in *frequent* use is quite limited, however, and with only a modest effort, you can become familiar with them.

The location of each weather observation point is shown by a small station circle (a square is used on most marine radiofacsimile charts). The weather information reported by each observer is coded for transmission and decoded for plotting on the map. It is plotted around the station circle in specific positions so that the data found in that same position for other stations always represent the same type of information. The only exception to this is for wind direction and speed, the position for which depends upon the actual compass direction of the wind.

Some of the information plotted around the station circle is self-explanatory. Other pieces of information, such as the nature of cloud types, require additional clarification and explanation.

Tables 14 to 26 in Appendix A provide clarification of map notations. Because the weather information plotted for each station varies in degree of completeness, it is best to examine the complete station plot first to recognize the simplified versions that are commonplace.

Weather data is coded for transmission and must be decoded for plotting on the map. The code consists of groups of five digits, with each group and each digit representing a specific combination or individual piece of weather data by its position in the transmission. Each piece of information has a *standard abbreviation*. Only the *numbers* are transmitted. The abbreviations are provided here only to identify the meaning of the numbers and their position in the transmission sequence. The example at the bottom of this page represents the transmission from only *one* weather station, for only one-time of observation. Data from many other stations will follow, and all new data will be transmitted by all stations at other hours of observation. In the example, only the numbers would be transmitted. Study the following explanation and examine Table 11.1.

The first group of five digits (**IIiii**) is the station identifier group (called the **index number**). This group tells you where the station is located. The first two digits (**II,** called the block number), identify the region (country or geographic area). The next three digits of the index number (**iii**) are the international station number (405 is Washington, DC). Some 1000 stations are assigned to each block number.

Like this index-number group, the remaining five-digit groups consist of standard positions which are filled, in each coded transmission, with the appropriate numbers. Table 11.1 explains these positions and the meaning of the numbers which fill them in our example. The table also gives the ways in which these data would be plotted on a map.

IIiii	**Nddff**	**VVwwW**	**PPPTT**	**$N_hC_LhC_MC_H$**	**$T_dT_d$app**	**7RRR_ts**
72405	50415	12636	13214	47228	12718	73740

TABLE 11.1 Interpreting Symbols in a Coded Transmission

Number Used in Coded Transmission	Symbol for Position in 5-Digit Group	Symbol to Appear on Map	Explanation
5	N	◐	Total amount of cloud cover. The Code Number 5 indicates that clouds cover 6/10 of the sky. See Table 15.
04	dd	(shaft from NE)	Wind direction. The code number 04 indicates that the wind is blowing from the northeast, 040° off true north. The shaft will be plotted.
15	ff	(barb symbol)	Wind speed. The code number 15 means a speed of 15 kn (17 MPH). See Table 16.
12	VV	3/4	Horizontal visibility. Code 12 means a visibility of 12/16 or 3/4 mi. The **VV** code is in 16ths of a mile through code 50 (3 1/8 mi). Use Table 17 for higher code numbers. Plot values to nearest whole mile for visibilities above 3 1/8 mi up to 10 mi. Visibilities of 10 mi and greater are not plotted on map.
63	ww	:•	Present weather. Continuous rain, moderate at time of observation, not freezing. See Table 18.
6	W	•	Past Weather. Was rain (within past 6 hr for 0000, 0600, 1200, and 1800 GMT reports; within past 3 hr for 0300, 0900, 1500, and 2100 GMT reports). See Table 19.
132	PPP	132	Air pressure. Pressure, reduced to sea level, is 1013.2 mb. Although only the coded three digits are plotted on most maps, the student is advised to plot the full value with the decimal and missing 9 or 10 added.
14	TT	57	Air temperature at time of observation. Observed in Fahrenheit, coded in Celsius, converted back to Fahrenheit for plotting on most maps (plotted in Celsius on marine radiofacsimile charts).
4	N_h	4	Lowest clouds cover 5/10 of the sky. See Table 15. (The code number is plotted.)
7	C_L	_ _ _	Low clouds. Fractostratus and/or fractocumulus of bad weather (scud clouds). See Table 22.
2	h	2	Height of the cloud base. Base at 300–599 ft. See Table 20. (The code number is plotted.)
2	C_M	⫽	Middle clouds. Altostratus or thick nimbostratus. See Table 23.
8	C_H	⌒	High clouds are cirrostratus, not covering the entire sky. See Table 24.
12	$T_d T_d$	54	Dew-point temperature. Coded in Celsius, converted and plotted on map in Fahrenheit.
7	a	\	Pressure tendency. Falling, steadily or unsteadily, but now lower than 3 hr ago. See Table 25.
18	pp	−1.8	Net change in pressure. In the past 3 hrs. −1.8 mb. Coded in tenths without the decimal point. The pressure tendency (**a**) determines whether this change is + or −.
7	7	None	The first digit of the sixth group after the index number is an **indicator figure.** It identifies this as special data group: 7 = *precipitation group.* Nothing is plotted.
37	RR	37	Amount of precipitation. In the 6 hr preceding the actual time of observation precipitation totaled 0.37 in. Includes snow as water equivalent.
4	R_t	4	Time of precipitation. The reported precipitation began 3 to 4 hr ago. See Table 26. The code number is plotted.
0	s	0	Depth of snow. Zero. The total accumulated depth of frozen precipitation, including snow, hail, and sleet, up to 8 in. is reported. Accumulations greater than 8 in. are reported in another special group, group 9, *special phenomena.* (See Table 11.2.) Not plotted on the map.

A model station plot is shown below. The information is shown by the use of the standard abbreviations, not the actual data, in order to emphasize the proper *placement* of the information.

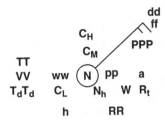

For the weather data decoded from the previous teletype transmission, a completed station plot of the information is shown below.

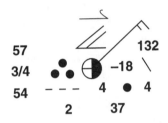

This example represents only *one* weather station at *one* time of observation. There are over 10,000 such land stations in the world, plus as many as 7000 aircraft and ship reports, plus many thousands of upper-air observations and automatic picture transmissions (APTs) from satellites. In a given 24-hr period there may be over 100,000 observations made. It is little wonder that high-speed computers are used to decode, plot, and analyze most of this data.

The kind of report we have examined is called the **primary message** (or the **6-hourly report** or **SYNOP**), with standard hours of observation of 0000, 0600, 1200, and 1800 GMT. In addition, an **intermediate synoptic** or **3-hourly report** is transmitted for 0300, 0900, 1500, and 2100 GMT. Some of the five-digit groups of weather information are **mandatory** (also called **universal**) and some are **supplementary** (such as the **7RRR$_t$s** group).

Some of the additional weather information that is collected, including that common to ship reports, is described in Table 11.2.

TABLE 11.2   Additional Weather Information in Some Coded Transmissions

Symbol for Position in Five-digit Group	Explanation
$D_H D_M D_L$	Direction from which high, middle, or low clouds are moving.
$d_w d_w$	True direction from which ocean waves are coming.
$H_w H_w$	Height of the waves.
$P_w P_w$	Period of the waves.
$P_{24} P_{24}$	Pressure change for the last 24 hr
$T_n T_n$	Minimum temperature.
$T_x T_x$	Maximum temperature.
$9 S_P S_P S_P S_P$	Special phenomena: snow depth over 8 in.; detailed information about blizzards, hurricanes, tornadoes; extreme variations in wind speed or direction or in visibility or air pressure; the occurrence of frost; frontal passages; depth of new-fallen snow; glaze and icing storms.
$6 P_o P_o P_o P_o$	Station pressure group—*not* reduced to sea level as is **PPP**. Pressure of 1000.0 or greater is coded with a 3: 1000.0 = 3000; 1012.5 = 3125; 986.5 = 9865.
$2 R_{24} R_{24} R_{24} R_{24}$	Twenty-four-hour precipitation group; 24-hour period preceding the 6-hourly report; reported by all U.S. stations where 0.01 in. or more has occurred; in tens, units, tenths, and hundreds, so 11.45 in. = 1145.
99ppp	Excessive pressure tendency group: If the pressure tendency net change is 9.9 mb or more, pp is reported as 99 and a special group (**99ppp**) follows immediately. Thus, $T_d T_d$**app** becomes $T_d T_d$**a99** followed by 99ppp. If the pressure change in 3 hr is 23.4 mb, the two code groups would be $T_d T_d$a99 99234.

ADDITIONAL NOTES

Solidi. Whenever a piece of information cannot be reported, for any reason, a solidus (/) is reported for each digit that is missing. If the pressure change (**pp**) is missing, solidi are reported as / / and the T_dT_d**app** group would appear as 122/ /.

Showers. A somewhat confusing term (present weather codes 80–90). Showers are *not* associated with thunder. They must be taking place at the time of the observation to be reported. They are from *isolated* clouds (usually convective clouds). Showers are normally of short duration, start and stop suddenly, and change intensity rapidly. They are normally associated with openings in the clouds between showers and with rapid change in sky appearance.

Temperature. When the temperature is *below zero* (*Celsius*), the number 50 is added to the actual Celsius value for coding. A temperature of –3°C would be coded and transmitted as 53 (for **TT** or T_dT_d). When received in a message, the number 50 or higher is decoded by first subtracting 50 and then converting to Fahrenheit.

name   section   date

Exercises

11.1 The following weather data have already been decoded. You are to plot this information in the proper positions around the station circles below.

Station	N	dd	ff	VV	ww	W	PPP	TT	Nh	CL	h	CM	CH	TdTd	a	pp	RR	Rt	s
1	1/10		0		[symbol]		068	36					[symbol]	34	/	25			
2	10/10	WSW	5	6	[symbol]	•	123	64	8	[symbol]	3	[symbol]		63	/	7	126	8	
3	9/10	NNW	15	7	[symbol]	[symbol]	150	27	8		2	[symbol]		25	[symbol]	14	03	7	
4	5/10	NW	18	20	[symbol]	[symbol]	155	25					[symbol]	16	[symbol]	12	09	4	
5	3/10	WSW	10				265	16						9	[symbol]	22			7
6	8/10	SE	25				218	55						48	[symbol]	10			
7	2/10	NE	5	3/8			383	34						27	[symbol]	14			
8	7/10	NW	55	1/8	[symbol]	≡	975	41	8	– – –				41	[symbol]	31	67	3	

(1) ◯

(2) ◯

(3) ◯

(4) ◯

(5) ◯

(6) ◯

(7) ◯

(8) ◯

name   section   date
_____

11.2 Using the data from the previous exercise, answer the following:

  a. What is the present weather (ww) at Station 1?

  b. What is the present weather (ww) at Station 2?

  c. What is the present weather (ww) at Station 3?

  d. What is the present weather (ww) at Station 4?

  e. What is the present weather (ww) at Station 8?

  f. What is the past weather (W) at Station 4?

  g. What is the past weather (W) at Station 8?

  h. What are the low clouds (C_L) at Station 2?

  i. What are the middle clouds (C_M) at Station 2?

  j. What are the high clouds (C_H) at Station 1?

  k. What are the high clouds (C_H) at Station 4?

  l. What are the middle clouds (C_M) at Station 3?

name   section   date

11.3 *Decode* the following teletype transmissions and plot the weather information in the proper positions.

Station	Nddff	VVwwW	PPPTT	$N_hC_LhC_MC_H$	$T_dT_d$app	$7RRR_ts$
1	71815	48805	18713	47231	10511	72110
2	20705	50011	17227	21500	15106	70000
3	71915	32645	98308	55621	06717	76130
4	83540	04757	93758	67404	59513	71237

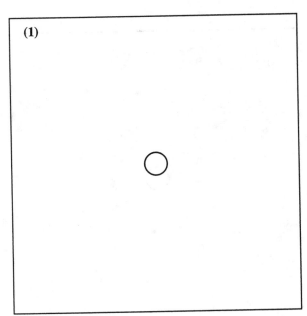

(1)

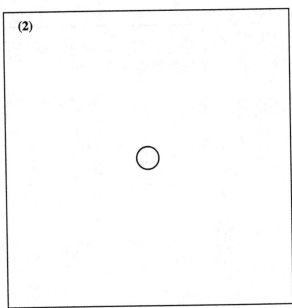

(2)

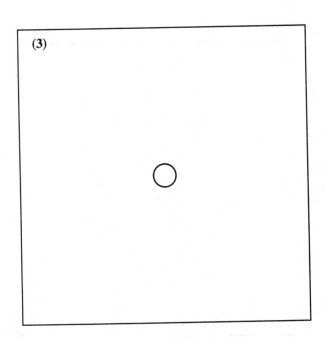

(3)

(4)

11.4 *Decode* the following teletype weather messages and plot the weather information in the proper positions.

Station	Nddff	VVwwW	PPPTT	$N_hC_LhC_MC_H$	$T_dT_d$app	$7RRR_ts$
1	81415	08367	98502	87122	02741	73540
2	52325	05312	15814	49363	10837	70710
3	92015	12040	00008	00000	04206	70000
4	20905	58010	13621	00000	13211	70000

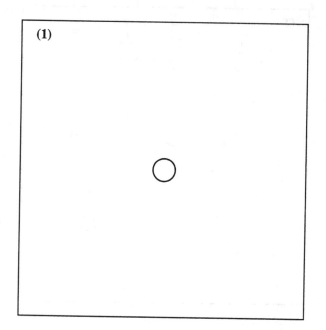

(1)

(2)

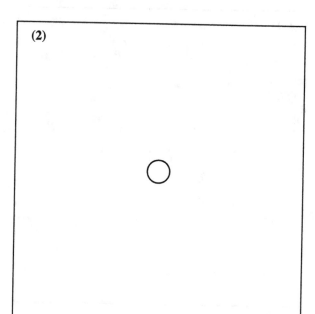

(3)

(4)

name   section   date

11.5   From Table 18 in Appendix A, Present Weather (**ww**), place the appropriate weather symbol in each of the following boxes:

	Snow	**Rain**	**Drizzle**
Intermittent, slight at time of observation			
Intermittent, moderate at time of observation			
Intermittent, heavy at time of observation			
Continuous slight at time of observation			
Continuous moderate at time of observation			
Continuous heavy at time of observation			
Freezing, slight			
Freezing, moderate or heavy			

	Rain Showers	**Thunderstorm**	**Fog**
During past hour but NOT at time of observation			
	Fog	**Slight or Moderate duststorm**	
No change in past hour			
Decreasing or thinning during past hour			
Increasing or thickening in past hour			

name   section   date

11.6   From Table 18 in Appendix A, copy the correct present weather (**ww**) symbol in the following boxes:

dust devil:	sleet:	squall:	light fog:
lightning, without thunder:	heavy thunderstorm with hail:	fog, depositing rime, sky not discernable:	funnel cloud:

11.7   From the three cloud tables in Appendix A, Tables 22, 23, and 24, copy the correct cloud symbol in the following boxes:

cirrus, dense:	stratus:	cumulus:	nimbostratus:
cumulonimbus without cirrus:	strato-cumulus:	fractostratus:	altocumulus, thin:

11.8   Using information from Table 5 in Appendix A, Nautical Miles, Statute Miles, and Kilometers, answer the following questions on the lines provided:

   a.   203 nautical mi = _____ statute mi

   b.   666 nautical mi = _____ statute mi

   c.   70 statute mi = _____ nautical mi

   d.   850 statute mi = _____ nautical mi

   e.   40 km = _____ statute mi

   f.   1000 km = _____ statute mi

   g.   480 statute mi = _____ km

   h.   20 statute mi = _____ km

name   section   date

11.9 In your own words, completely describe the weather at 7:00 A.M. for the following places. Use Map 12.11 for Saturday, November 22, on page 190.

a. Houston, Texas:

b. Boise, Idaho:

c. Astoria, Washington:

d. Churchill, Ontario:

e. Burlington, Vermont:

f. Montreal, Quebec:

g. Rapid City, South Dakota:

h. Salt Lake City, Utah:

i. Forth Worth, Texas:

j. Shreveport, Louisiana:

11.10 Convert the following times as directed.

    a.   0000Z to eastern standard time   _____

    b.   0600Z to mountain standard time   _____

    c.   12Z to eastern daylight time   _____

    d.   18Z to Alaskan standard time   _____

    e.   0300 GMT to eastern standard time   _____

    f.   2100Z to eastern daylight time   _____

    g.   1230Z to Pacific standard time   _____

    h.   1040Z to central standard time   _____

11.11 Convert the following standard times to GMT.

    a.   10:45 A.M. EST to GMT   _____

    b.   9:30 P.M. EST to GMT   _____

    c.   12:10 P.M. CST to GMT   _____

    d.   3:00 A.M. PST to GMT   _____

name   section   date

Review and Study Questions

1.   What is the difference between an *analysis* weather map and a *prognosis* weather map?

2.   What does *synoptic* mean?

3.   What is a *nephanalysis* map?

4.   What is the difference between a *primary* weather message and an *intermediate* weather message?

5.   What is meant by *significant weather?*

6.   What lengths of time are involved in *extended* forecasts?

7.   A variety of weather data are typically plotted for each station on a surface analysis map. Describe a few examples of such data that are "self-explanatory" and a few examples of plotted data that cannot be so easily interpreted.

8.   What is the significance of understanding the *Valid Time* (VT) on a weather map before using such a map?

9.   What different kinds of weather maps and charts are commonly presented by your local television weather-person in the weather segment of the evening news program?

10.   Although there are 100 different plotting symbols to depict the single piece of information called *Present Weather* (ww), many are simply different combinations of the same basic symbol. Name and give the symbol for several of the most basic symbols.

chapter *12*

WEATHER ANALYSIS and FORECASTING

Chapter 11 suggested the vast quantity of synoptic information and other weather data collected and reported daily to the National Weather Service, which prepares a vast array of weather maps and charts from this information. In addition, a wide range of mathematical and physical models of the atmosphere are used to assimilate this data for numerical guidance and forecasting. The science of meteorology is complex and intricate, and weather forecasting is one of its most involved and intricate aspects.

Several fundamental predictive relationships were introduced in earlier chapters. Seasonal changes in pressure, wind, and temperature resulting from changes in earth–sun relationships are cyclically predictable. Pressure changes (as measured by barometers) help to predict both short and long-range weather conditions. Pressure fields are related to wind-flow patterns, and wind and air motions help to indicate future weather. Predictions of the movement of warmer, colder, drier, or more humid air masses into or out of a given region are fundamental to basic weather forecasts. Air-flow patterns of convergence and divergence, the amount of precipitable water in the air, conditions of atmospheric stability or instability, and the direction and speed of movement of weather fronts are all fundamental predictors of weather changes as well as explanations of existing conditions.

These basic conditions must first be analyzed so that we understand the *current* weather conditions. Only then can such factors be used to *forecast* the changes in the weather that might occur and the magnitude and timing of these changes. Such analyses, and the forecasts based upon them, may be categorized as: air-mass analysis, frontal analysis, isobaric analysis, upper-air analysis, nephanalysis, radar analysis, and others.

The following exercises continue our study of the weather map and synoptic weather data, introduce some practice at analyzing the data, and require some basic forecasting of future weather conditions.

Drawing Isobars

The section in Chapter 1 on isopleths **should be reviewed.** Special adjustments to isobars as they cross weather fronts, to show the sometimes sharp kinks that "point" towards higher pressure along the front, must now be practiced. It is important to remember that all initial work on the weather map should be done *lightly* in pencil. Adjustments of the initial positioning of fronts and isobars is almost always necessary as the analysis of the data progresses. Extreme wiggles, bends, and kinks in fronts and isopleths (often unavoidable for the first approximation) should be eliminated as much as possible in the final depiction. (Kinks in the isobars as they cross a front are frequently the exception.) Only when all final adjustments have been completed and thoroughly checked for accuracy should the fronts and isobars be gone over and darkened for legibility. All previous approximations should be thoroughly erased.

The numerical value of each isobar should be clearly labeled, and the labels should not interfere with other plotted data on the map. Isobars should be labeled in more than one place, for clarity, especially when they are extensive. The labels of the isobars should be aligned, as much as possible, in a sequence in a given area or areas on the map. A study of the surface weather maps in this chapter will clearly show how the isobars should be labeled.

Pressure data are plotted on the map to the nearest tenth of a millibar, with the decimal point and the initial 9 or 10 omitted. It is usually easier for the student to add back the initial 9 or 10 and the decimal point before beginning the task of drawing isobars. Fewer errors will result, especially in the first few maps done. Note that the values of isobars are labeled as whole numbers (with no decimal points) on the surface weather maps in this chapter. Another common method (especially on facsimile maps) is to label only the figures for units and tens in the value of the isobar. Data presented according to these two methods would appear as:

— 996 —	or	— 96 —
— 1000 —	or	— 00 —
— 1004 —	or	— 04 —

Although no two people will approach the tasks of frontal analysis and isobaric analysis in exactly the same way, I recommend that you try to locate the weather fronts *before* drawing the isobars. When you draw the isobars, it may be helpful to start working *outward* from a *cell* of high or low pressure. To find such cells, first examine the overall pressure field from the plotted pressure data.

name   section   date

Exercises

12.1 a. On Map 12.1(a):

    1. Locate and draw in the front(s) with the proper symbol(s).

    2. Draw the isobars using a 4-mb interval (to include the 1000-mb isobar).

    3. Draw in *five thunderstorm symbols* in locations where they most likely belong.

b. On Map 12.1(b):

    1. Locate and draw in the front(s) with the proper symbol(s).

    2. Draw the isobars using a 4-mb interval (to include the 1000-mb isobar).

    3. Add cloud symbols at the weather stations where they are most likely to be found, for the following:

        nimbostratus
        stratus
        altostratus
        cirrostratus
        cirrus
        cumulus

name   section   date

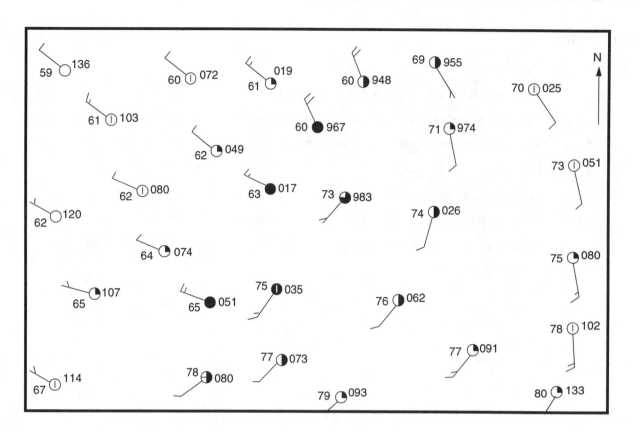

Map 12.1(a)   (For Exercise 12.1a.)

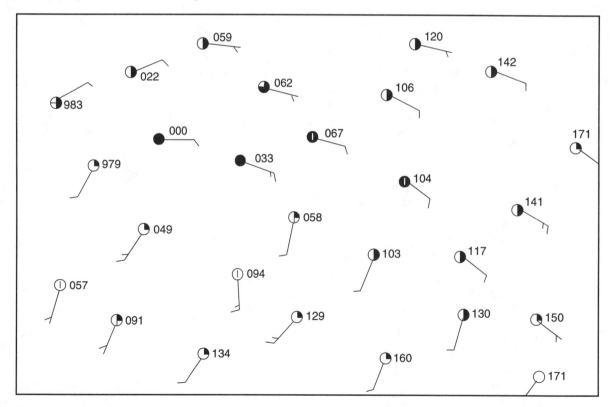

Map 12.1(b)   (For Exercise 12.1b.)

name   section   date
_____

12.2 On the following simplified weather map, Map 12.2, indicate the following:

   a. Frontal analysis. Locate and draw in the weather front(s) using the proper symbol(s).

   b. Isobaric analysis.

      1. Draw in the isobars using a 4-mb interval that includes the 1000-mb isobar. Label all isobars in the proper way.

      2. Identify the center(s) of pressure cell(s) by printing the proper letter symbol(s) in the correct locations on the map.

   c. Air-mass analysis. Identify the air masses by printing the proper air mass symbol(s) on the map.

   d. Precipitation analysis. Only after all of the above analyses are *perfect* and *final* show the likely areas of precipitation by *lightly* shading in all such areas.

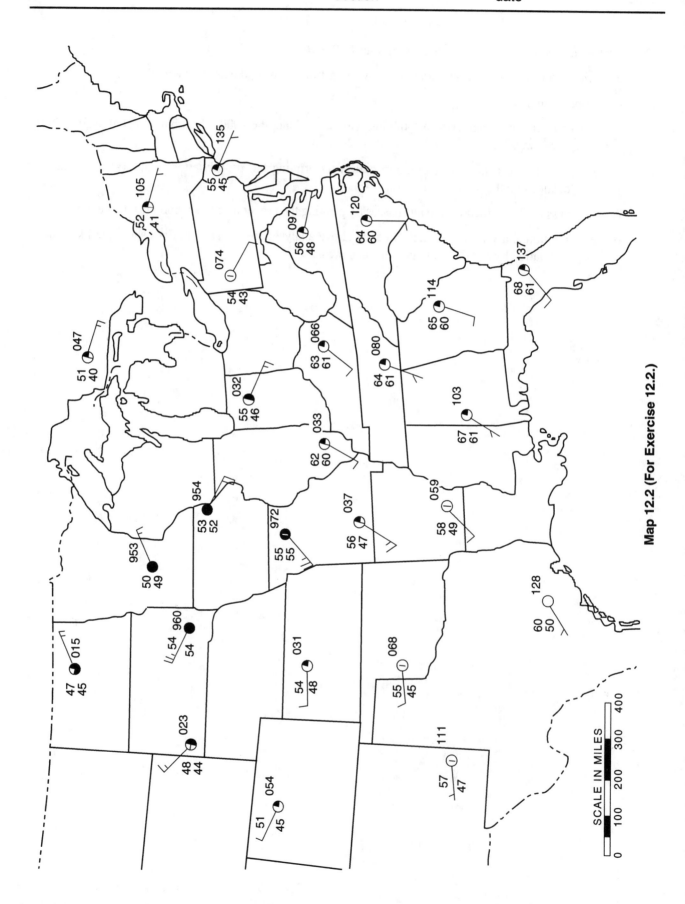

Map 12.2 (For Exercise 12.2.)

SCALE IN MILES

0   100   200   300   400

name   section   date

12.3 On Map 12.3:

    a. Locate and draw in the weather front(s) using the proper symbol(s).

    b. Draw in the isobars using a 4-mb interval which includes the 1000-mb isobar. Label all isobars in the proper way.

    c. Label the center(s) of pressure areas with the proper letter symbol(s).

name   section   date

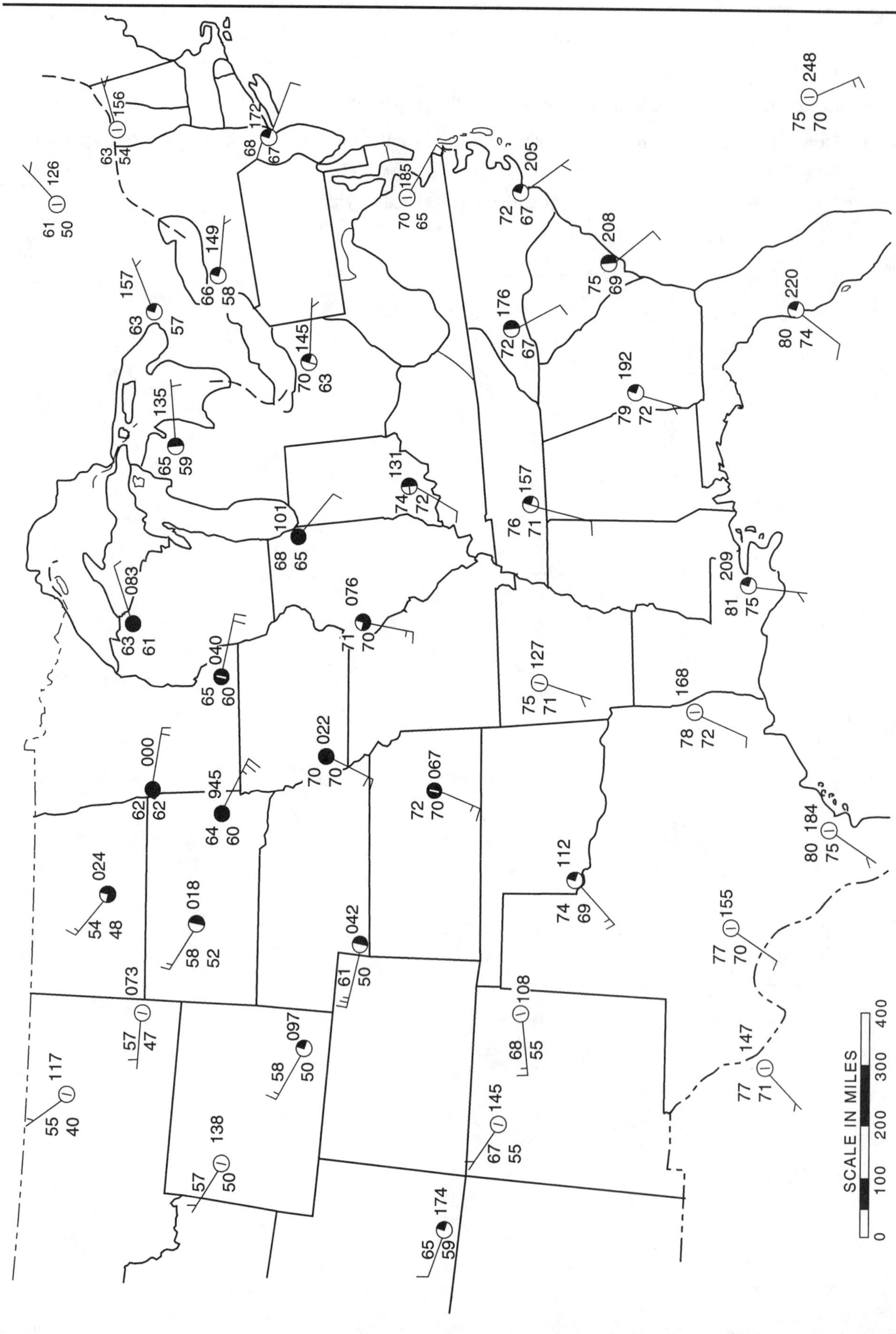

Map 12.3

SCALE IN MILES

0   100   200   300   400

name   section   date

12.4 a. On Map 12.4 on the next page, do the following:

    1. Locate and draw in the weather front(s) using the proper symbol(s).

    2. Draw in the isobars using a 4-mb interval which includes the 1000-mb isobar. Label all isobars in the proper way.

    3. Label the pressure field with the proper letter symbol(s).

  b. If we assume the front(s) are moving eastward at 400 mi per day and that any low-pressure cells are intensifying:

    1. What *changes* in the present weather conditions in South Dakota may be expected *during* the next 24 hr?

    2. What weather changes should occur during the next 24 hr at the weather station in Wisconsin?

name section date

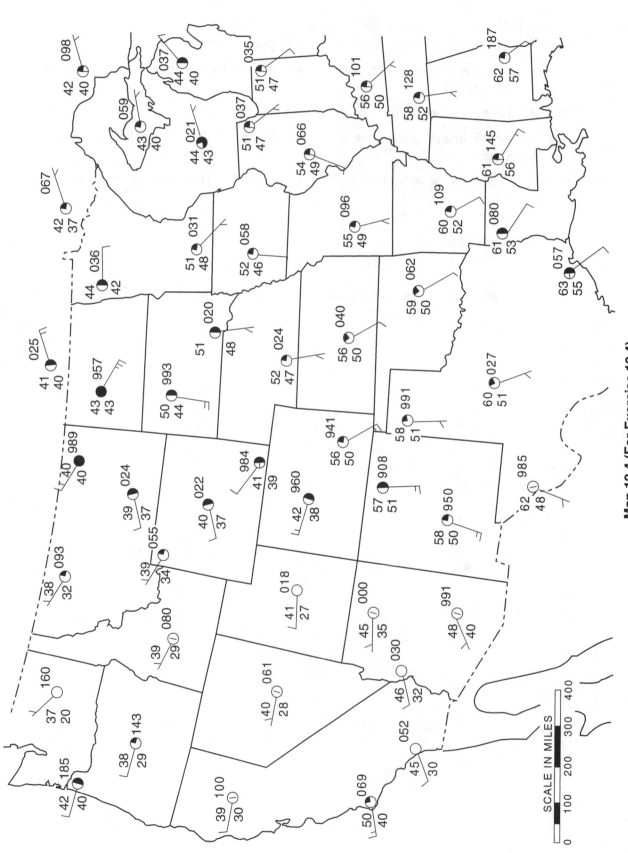

Map 12.4 (For Exercise 12.4)

name   section   date

12.5 a. On Map 12.5 do the following:

1. Locate and draw in the weather front(s) using the proper symbol(s).

2. Draw in the isobars using a 4-mb interval which includes the 1000-mb isobar. Label all isobars in the proper way.

3. Label significant pressure areas with the proper letter symbol(s).

b. Assuming that all cyclones and fronts continue to move in their apparent directions of advance at the rate of 600 mi per day:

1. What *new* kind of *frontal weather* should develop within 24 hr? Explain.

2. *Where* will this be occurring in 24 hr?

3. What new development, in terms of significant pressure cell(s), might be expected as a result of this occurrence, and *where* will it be in 24 hr?

c. Describe the humidity characteristics of the air masses shown on the map.

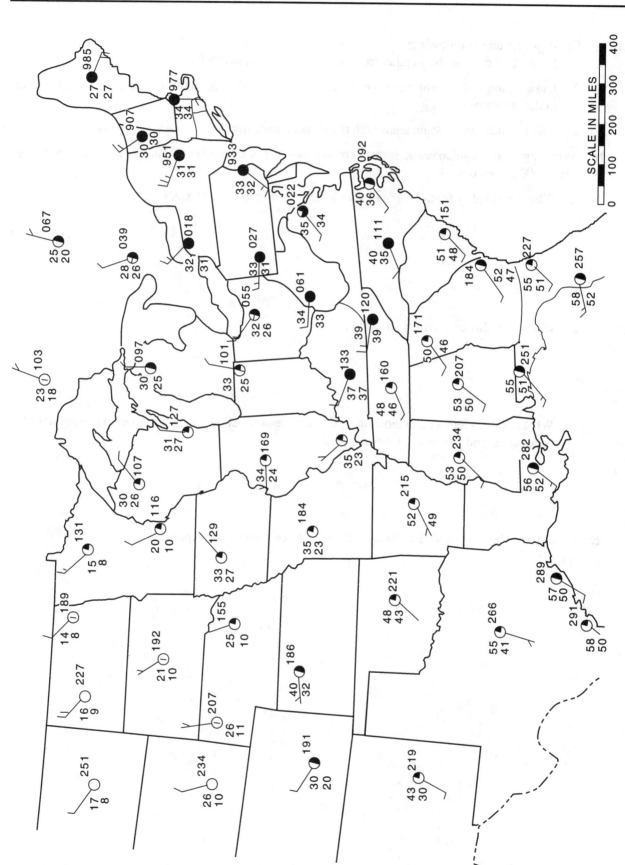

Map 12.5 (For Exercise 12.5)

SCALE IN MILES

0   100   200   300   400

name   section   date

12.6 Using the 7:00 A.M. reports for *Boston, Massachusetts,* during the week of November 17 through November 23 (Maps 12.6 to 12.12):

a. Fill in the appropriate data for each day in the following chart.

	17th		18th		19th		20th		21st		22nd		23rd		24th
Temperature															
Dew point															
Wind Direction															
Air pressure															
Cloud cover															

b. Place a checkmark (√) in the narrow columns between each pair of dates whenever the *change* in a weather element (between the two 7:00 A.M. reports) appears to be a *significant change.*

c. For each date, write a brief explanation of the causes of:

1. the *weather conditions* in Boston at 7:00 A.M. on that date, or

2. any *significant changes* in Boston's weather from the previous day.

November 17:

November 18:

November 19:

November 20:

November 21:

November 22:

November 23:

d. What do you think the weather elements will be on Monday, November 24? Fill in your *forecast* of these estimated values in the column provided for the 24th in the chart.

12.7 Using the 7:00 A.M. reports for *Moline, Illinois,* during the week of November 17 through November 23 (Maps 12.6 to 12.12):

a. Fill in the appropriate data for each day in the following chart.

	17th		18th		19th		20th		21st		22nd		23rd		24th
Temperature															
Dew point															
Wind Direction															
Air pressure															
Cloud cover															

b. Place a checkmark (√) in the narrow columns between each pair of dates whenever the *change* in a weather element (between the two 7:00 A.M. reports) appears to be a *significant change.*

c. For each date, write a brief explanation of the *causes* of:

1. the *weather conditions* at Moline at 7:00 A.M. on that date, or

2. any *significant changes* in Moline's weather from the previous day.

November 17:

November 18:

November 19:

November 20:

November 21:

November 22:

November 23:

d. What do you think the weather elements will be on Monday, November 24? Fill in your *forecast* of these estimated values in the column provided for the 24th in the chart.

name section date

Map 12.6 Monday, November 17.

SURFACE WEATHER MAP
AND STATION WEATHER
AT 7:00 A.M., E.S.T.

POLAR STEREOGRAPHIC PROJECTION TRUE AT LATITUDE 60°
SCALE OF NAUTICAL MILES AT VARIOUS LATITUDES

name   section   date

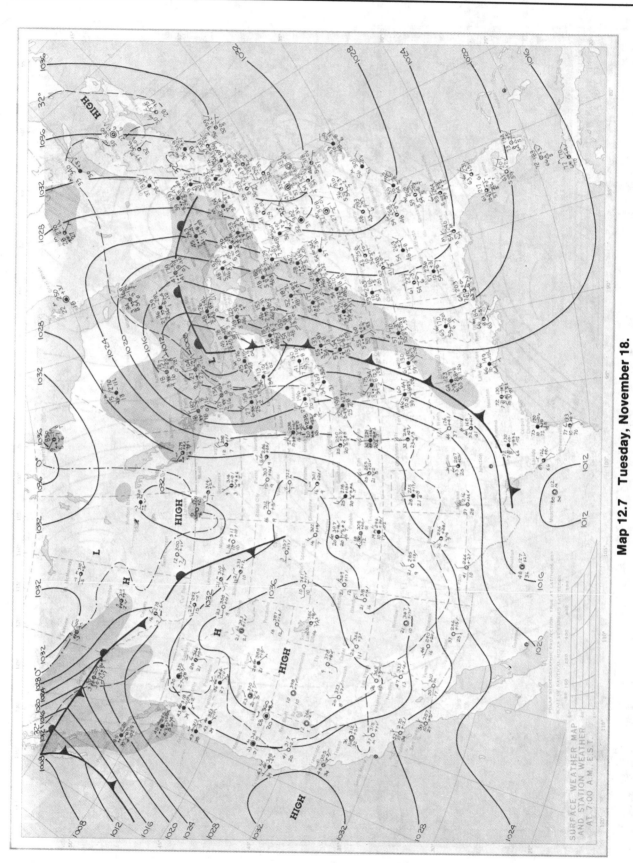

Map 12.7   Tuesday, November 18.

name section date

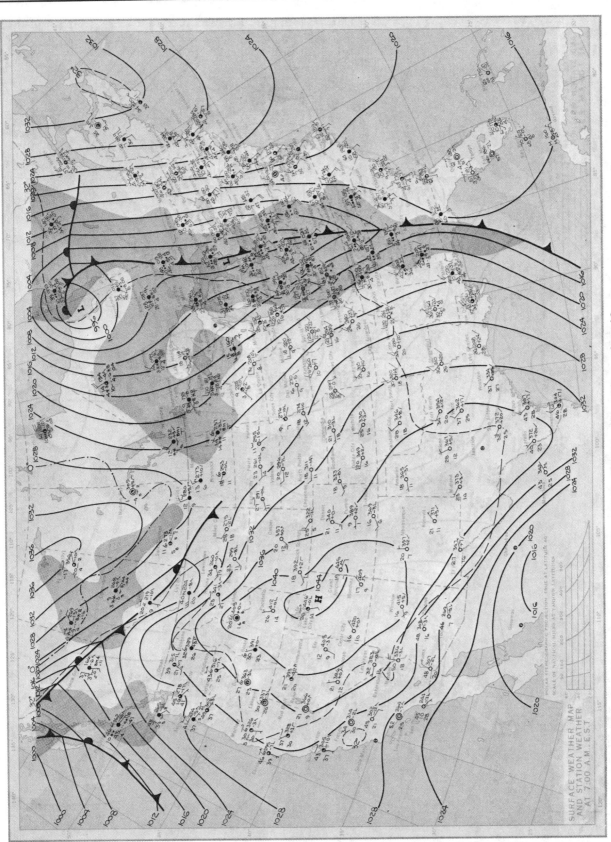

Map 12.8   Wednesday, November 19.

name   section   date

Map 12.9   Thursday, November 20.

name   section   date

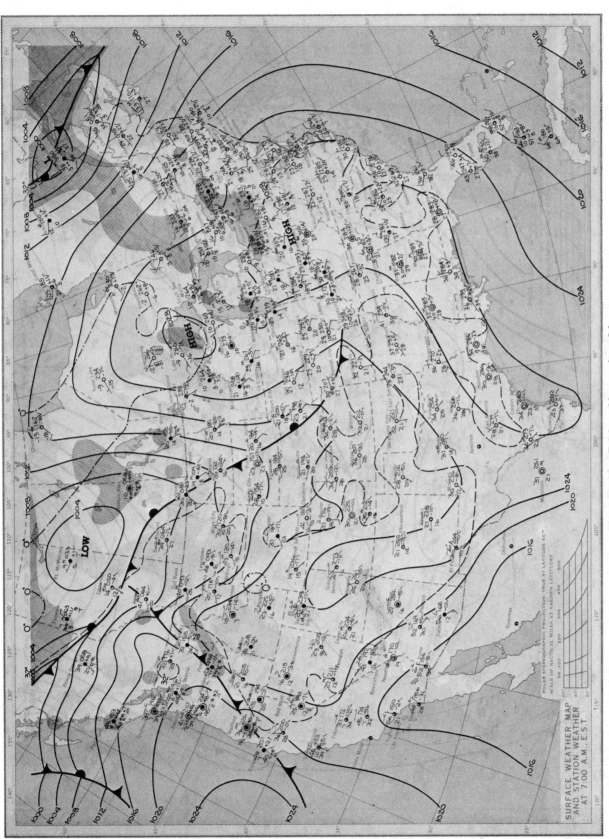

Map 12.10   Friday, November 21.

name section date

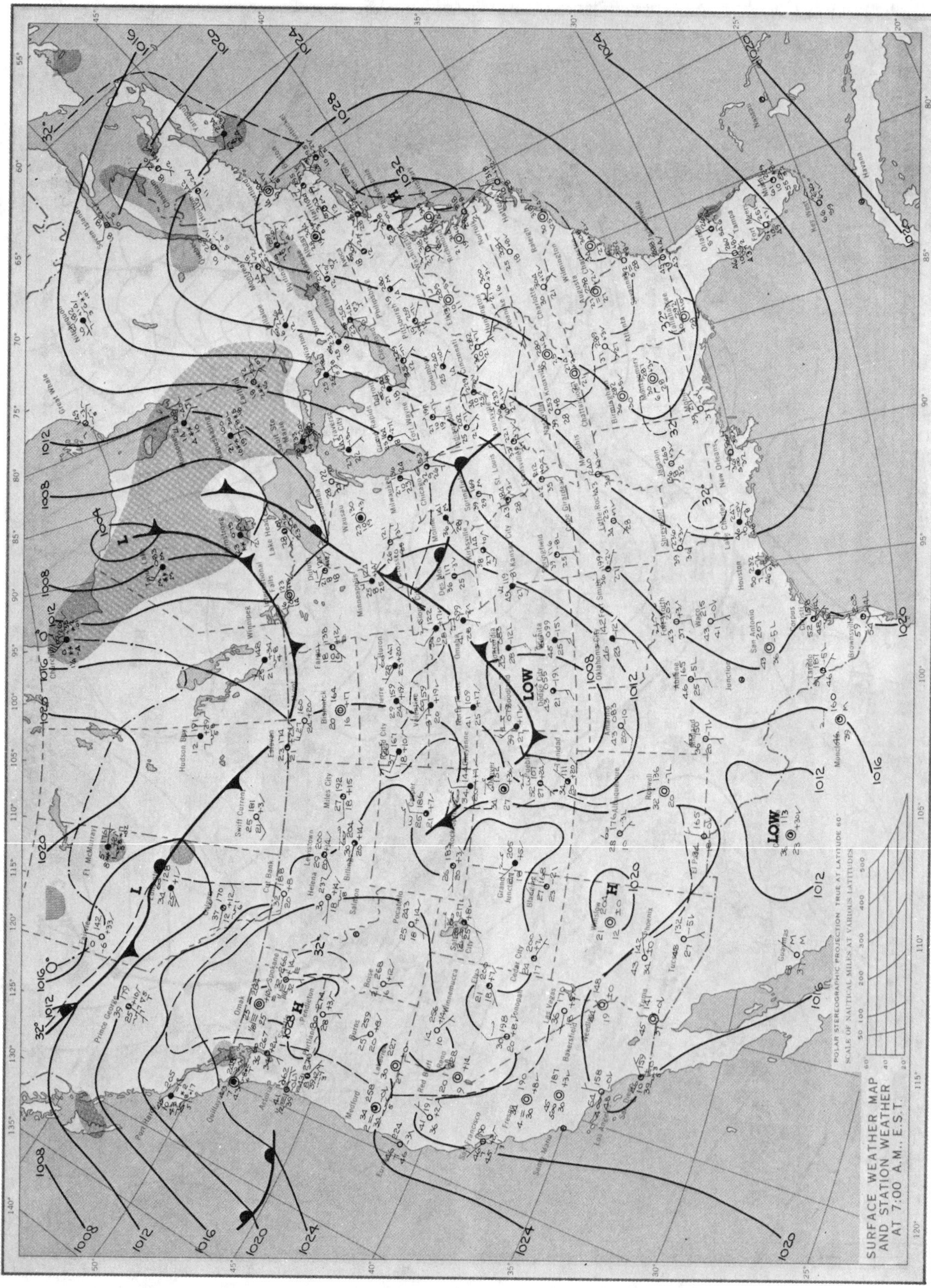
SURFACE WEATHER MAP AND STATION WEATHER AT 7:00 A.M., E.S.T.
POLAR STEREOGRAPHIC PROJECTION TRUE AT LATITUDE 60°
SCALE OF NAUTICAL MILES AT VARIOUS LATITUDES
LOW
LOW
H
H
L
L

Map 12.11 Saturday, November 22.

name   section   date

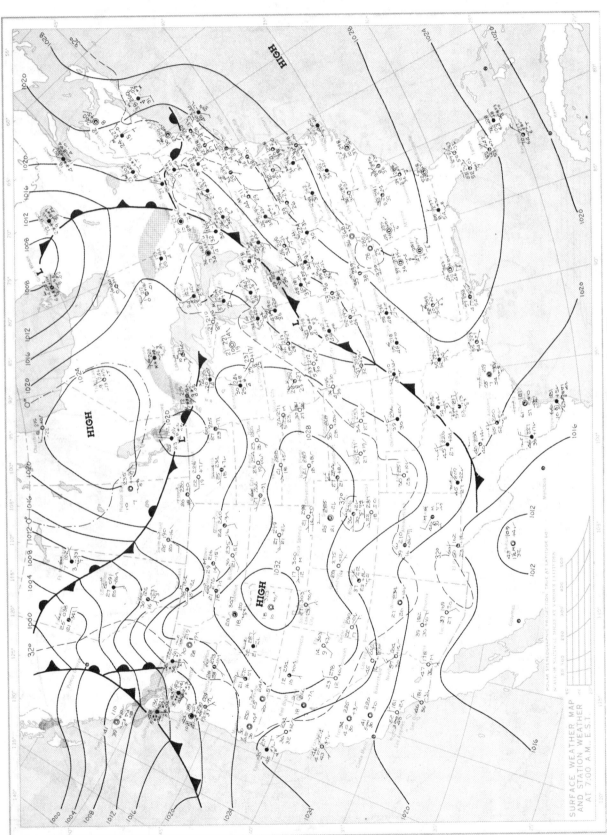

Map 12.12   Sunday, November 23.

name   section   date

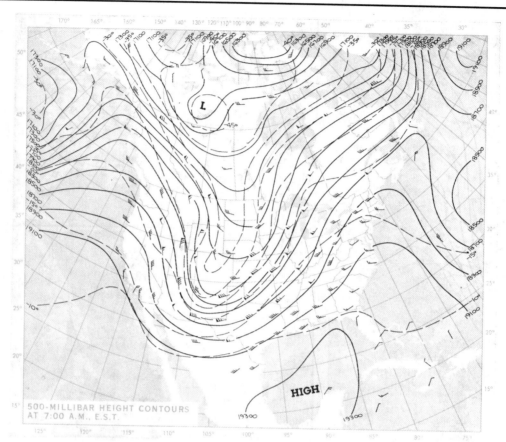

Map 12.13   Tuesday, November 18.

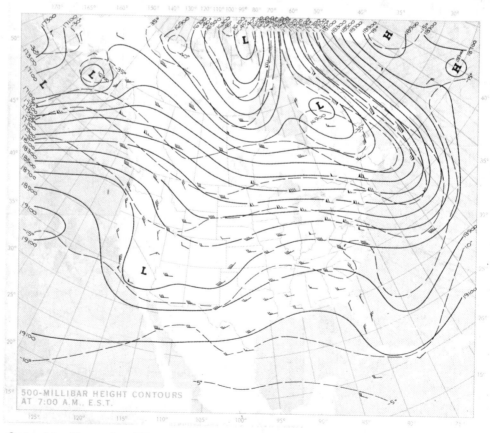

Map 12.14   Saturday, November 22.

name   section   date

12.8 From Maps 12.11 and 12.12, for Saturday, November 22, and Sunday, November 23, we can see that the frontal system in the central part of the United States has moved northeastward. The southern part of the cold front has moved more rapidly and has straightened out. The cold front has moved northeastward at about 500 mi per day while the warm front has moved northeastward at about 700 mi per day. The occluded front has slowed down and is showing a more pronounced backward bend. The low-pressure cell centered in Kansas on the 22nd has also moved northeastward along the front at about 500 mi per day to its position in Illinois on the 23rd.

Now *assume* the following:

a. The cold front continues to move at the same speed and in the same direction for the next 24 hr.
b. The warm front also continues to move at the same speed and in the same direction.
c. The occluded front continues to move with the system, except for its northernmost position, which remains near Great Whale, Quebec.
d. The weak low-pressure cell (in Illinois on the 23rd) *intensifies* while moving 300 mi to the northeast along the cold front.

Using Map 12.15 (blank), draw in the *positions* that you *forecast* for this frontal system. (Draw your prognosis for all three fronts and the new position of the intensified low-pressure cell.)

12.9 The frontal system in the Pacific Northwest (in British Columbia, Canada) on November 18 hardly moved at all over the 48 hr from the 18th to the 20th. Briefly explain the reasons for this lack of movement.

12.10 How does Map 12.13 (the 500-mb chart for 7:00 A.M. on Tuesday, November 18) help to explain why the low-pressure center moved from Lake Superior (on the 18th) almost due north to its position over James Bay in Canada on the 19th?

12.11 How does Map 12.14 (the 500-mb chart for 7:00 A.M. on Saturday, November 22) help to explain why the low-pressure area centered over Kansas on the 22nd moved much more eastward than northward from its Kansas position on the 22nd to its position in Illinois on Sunday, November 23?

name   section   date

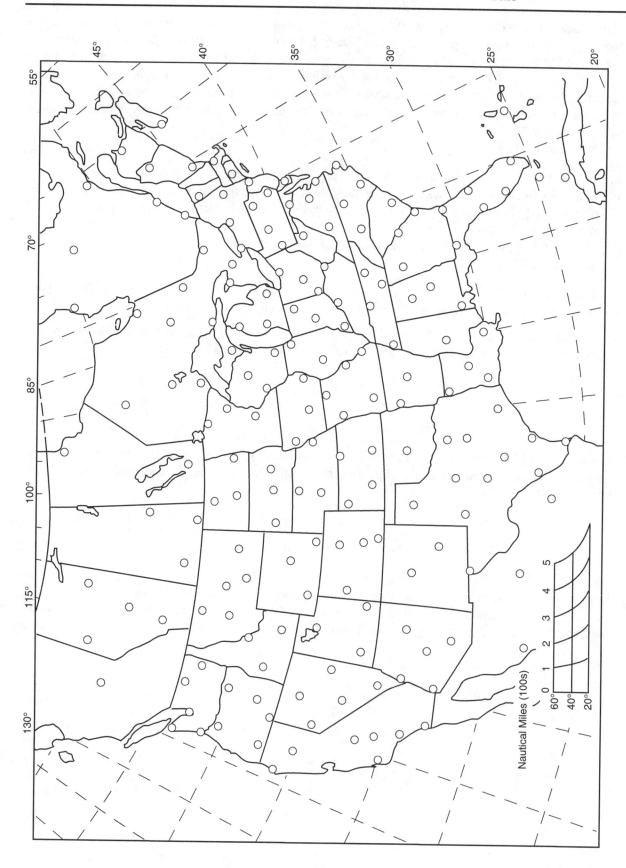

Map 12.15 (For Exercise 12.8)

Nautical Miles (100s)

name   section   date

12.12 A cyclonic storm, moving to the northeast, is shown below. Assume the cyclone is moving along the storm track (indicated by the dashed arrow) at 600 mi per day. *Forecast* the future weather conditions for selected stations by answering the following questions on the lines provided.

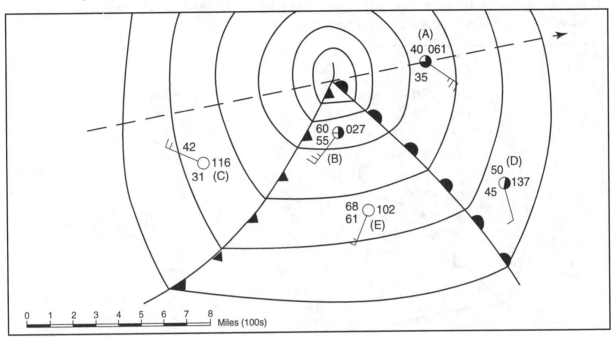

- **a.** In 24 hr, the pressure at Station A should be _____

- **b.** In 48 hr, the wind direction at Station A should be _____

- **c.** The center of the cyclone should be directly over Station A in how many hours? _____

- **d.** In 24 hr, the temperature at Station B should be _____

- **e.** In 24 hr, the pressure at Station B should be _____

- **f.** In 24 hr, the cloud coverage at Station B should be _____

- **g.** Station B should experience a rapid and significant drop in temperature how many hours from now? _____

- **h.** In 24 hr, the temperature at Station E should be _____

- **i.** In 24 hr, the pressure at Station E should be _____

- **j.** In 24 hr, the wind direction at Station E should be _____

- **k.** In 24 hr, the temperature at Station D should be _____

- **l.** In 24 hr, the pressure at Station D should be _____

- **m.** In 24 hr, the wind direction at Station D should be _____

- **n.** In 60 hr, the wind direction at Station D should be _____

- **o.** The storm is moving at how many miles *per hour?* _____

name   section   date

12.13 A cyclonic storm with associated frontal systems is shown below. Computer models have produced two conflicting predictions about the path the storm will take. One model predicts the storm will take Track X. A second model predicts Track Z. Both models predict the cold front will advance 500 miles per day for the next few days while the warm front will advance 400 miles per day. Both models predict no weakening nor intensification of the low pressure cell for the next few days.

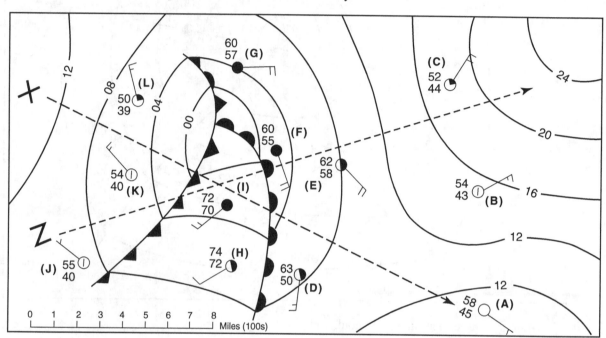

a.   Assuming Track X:

   1.   What is the average speed at which the *warm* front is advancing (in miles per hour)? _____ MPH

   2.   What is the average speed at which the *cold* front is advancing (in miles per hour)? _____ MPH

   3.   When should Station A experience a large *drop* in temperature?
         _____ hours;   _____ days

   4.   When should the *warm*-sector air get to Station A?
         Explain:

b.   Assuming Track Z:

   5.   When will Station F experience a rise in temperature (how many hours from now)?_____ hours

   6.   When will Station E experience a rise in temperature (how many hours from now)?_____ hours

   7.   If the data on the map is for 7:00 A.M. *today,* then when (what clock time) should
         Station F expect a wind shift to the northwest?   _____

   8.   Assuming the low pressure center neither weakens nor intensifies, what should be
         the pressure at Station C about 54 hours from now?   _____ mb

name   section   date

Review and Study Questions

1. What are the fundamental differences between weather *analysis* and weather *forecasting?*

2. What specific aspects of the atmosphere and its weather are commonly analyzed and forecast?

3. Weather forecasting is often described as an art as well as a science. Do you agree or disagree, and what are your reasons for your position?

4. The *persistence forecast* is based on the recent history of a weather event or pattern and is a projection of that recent weather history into the immediate future (usually six to twelve hours, often less). In the case of a cyclonic storm, what would you want to know about the storm's recent history in order to make a persistence forecast for your area?

5. The *meteorological forecast* does not simply assume the continuation of the recent past and requires more information than a persistence forecast. What additional tools, information, and guidance would you seek to obtain and use if you had to make a 48-hour meteorological forecast for your area?

6. The *climatological forecast* is based on long-term weather data and our understanding of the annual change of the seasons. These cyclical changes of the seasons produce general changes in the local weather over periods of several weeks and months. Describe some of these seasonal weather changes for your area.

7. Assume that in early November you have to prepare a climatological forecast of the probability of a "white Christmas" for your area. What kind and quality of information would you seek? If you can find this information, what would be your prediction?

8. If you were given ten minutes to predict what the weather will be like during the next six to twelve hours, and you could use only one weather instrument and your own visual observations, what instrument would you choose? Give your reasons for your choice and explain how you would utilize that instrument to make your forecast.

chapter 13

CLIMATE and CLIMATIC ANALYSIS

Weather and climate are interrelated. One helps to describe and explain the other. While *weather* refers to the conditions that exist at a given moment, or for a relatively short period of time, *climate* refers to the long-term conditions described by the long-term averages and extremes of the weather. Climate is more than just the average of weather, however. Descriptions of climate must recognize the extremes, frequencies, and the variability of the elements. The *elements* are the same for both weather and climate (temperate, air pressure, wind, moisture, precipitation, sky conditions, etc.).

The role of climatic controls in influencing and explaining weather conditions has been treated in the previous chapters. The controls of latitude (earth–sun relationships and solar radiation), land and water differences (continental and maritime locations), elevation (altitude), landforms, ocean currents, global pressure patterns, and the general circulation of the atmosphere (winds), have all been used to explain weather conditions. These same controls, when sufficiently persistent over the years to be the dominant factor for a region, become the basis for describing the climate of the region. Commonplace terms for climates, such as *tropical, temperate, polar, arctic, subtropical*, and *mid-latitude* all suggest the primary control of latitude on one important element—temperature. *Mountain climate* suggests the role of elevation and landforms. *Continental* and *maritime* as terms for climate imply that land masses and water bodies receive and absorb solar radiation differently.

Many factors may influence changes in climate over periods of hundreds of years to tens of thousands of years. Changing levels of atmospheric constituents (carbon dioxide, ozone, particulate matter from human activities and volcanic activity), the effects of human beings and animals on the soil and vegetation cover of the earth (changing surface albedos), changes in solar output (variations in sunspot activity), and changes in the earth's motions and alignments as a planet in the solar system (orbital variations and polar wanderings) are all possible causes of long-term climatic changes. Some of these long-term factors may even influence short-term weather, although the problems in substantiating this claim are formidable.

As weather is related to climate, so climate is related to vegetation. The climatic conditions of temperature, moisture, and sunshine have an overwhelming influence on the natural vegetation of a region. Many terms used to describe a climatic region are names for a vegetation region as well. Such climate-vegetation terms include *savanna, rain forest, steppe, Mediterranean, desert, prairie, scrub, taiga, boreal*, and *tundra*. The definitions used for determining the boundaries of some climatic types are values related to the tolerance of vegetation. The value of 50°F for the warmest month separates the polar (**E**) climates from other, more temperate, climates. The isotherm for a warmest month of 50°F will show a reasonably good coincidence with the poleward boundary of the high-latitude forests. The value of 32°F for the warmest month separates the sparsely vegetated tundra (**ET** climate) from those regions devoid of vegetation throughout the entire year (**EF** climate). The temperate margin for many tropical plants coincides with the isotherm of 65°F for the coolest month. The rainfall pattern also closely relates to vegetation limits. The isohyet for 10-in. annual precipitation clearly defines the arid regions of the world, and the isohyet for 20-in. annual precipitation is a fair approximation of the semiarid regions. When precipitation is related to temperature (and evaporation rates), the correlation of evaporation and transpiration rates to vegetation is even closer.

Even the importance of soils to vegetation is climatically related. The weathering and erosion processes associated with soil formation, acting on the mineral composition of the bedrock, are strongly related to climatic conditions. As a result of these interrelationships, the world patterns of climate, vegetation, and soils show a high degree of coincidence. A study of world maps of climate, vegetation, and soils will show this coincidence, especially in the centers of the respective regions. The borders for such regions do not always coincide, because of basic differences in the phenomena themselves, the differences in the classification schemes used, and differences in establishing values for boundary transition zones. Nevertheless, relatively sharp boundary lines, coincident for climate, vegetation, and soils, do exist. Such sharp boundaries often correlate with landforms, and a world map of landforms will show coincidence in many areas with climate, vegetation, and soil patterns.

A study of climate will show a clear pattern of zonation based upon latitude. A comparable vertical zonation also exists in mountainous regions. In the mountainous areas of Latin America, for instance, climatic regions are often described according to elevation. The response of vegetation to elevation is very similar to the response of vegetation to latitude. Whether influenced by elevation or latitude, vegetation is temperature and moisture-dependent. In such low-altitude mountainous areas, the vertical zonation of climate and vegetation regions includes the *tierra caliente* (hot region; tropical vegetation), the *tierra templada* (temperate region; temperate crops including coffee), the *tierra fria* (cold region; hardy crops such as the grains and potatoes), and the *paramos* (alpine meadows; grasses for grazing), and ends with the zone of permanent snow. Thus, even though a mountain may be on the equator, if it is high enough it may include a climate zone of year-round cold not unlike the polar climate of the high latitudes. Such vertical climates will show changes in the species of trees, their density, and their size with increasing elevation up to the alpine meadows. Such variations are very similar to the changes that are found by moving latitudinally poleward through the great northern forests towards the tundra.

The Köppen System of Climate Classification

Many systems have been developed for analyzing and classifying climatic data and defining climatic regions. The Köppen system is one of the best-known and most frequently used systems. In the course of its use, it has undergone various modifications, sometimes simplifications and sometimes additional refinements. These modifications have been made by many different researchers (Russell, Shear, Trewartha, and others) over the years. The Köppen system (also called the Köppen–Geiger or Köppen–Geiger–Pohl system) recognizes five **primary classifications** of climate. Each of these five is further classified into several **secondary classifications,** and these have been divided into several **tertiary classifications.**

The primary classifications are the **A, B, C, D,** and **E** climates. These five classes, together with other common names for the same or broadly similar climatic types, are the following:

> **A** = Tropical (megathermal)
> **B** = Dry (arid and semiarid)
> **C** = Subtropical (mesothermal, temperate)
> **D** = Continental (microthermal, temperate)
> **E** = Polar (arctic, tundra, and icecap)

One modification of the Köppen system includes a sixth class, **H,** for highlands. Usually, an arbitrary value is selected, such as 5000 ft, to define the elevation above which all areas would be lumped together as undifferentiated climates.

A more complete classification incorporating secondary and tertiary classes in addition to the primary classes, provides the following types of climates:

> **Af** = Tropical rainy (tropical rain forest, tropical wet)
> **Am** = Tropical monsoon
> **Aw** = Tropical wet and dry (tropical savanna)
> **BS** = Semiarid (steppe)
> **BW** = Arid (desert)
> **Cfa** = Humid subtropical (warm and humid temperate)
> **Cfb, Cfc** = Mid-latitude temperate (marine, marine west coast)
> **Cw** = Subtropical monsoon (tropical and subtropical upland)

Csa, Csb = Mediterranean
Dfa, Dfw = Humid continental, hot summer; moist or dry winter
Dfb, Dwb = Humid continental, warm summer; moist or dry winter
Dfc, Dwc, Dfd, Dwd = Subarctic; long, cold winter
ET = Tundra (arctic, polar)
EF = Icecap (arctic, perpetual frost, polar)

The Köppen definitions for each of the above symbols, definitions that are the basis for classifying climatic data and for delineation of climatic regions, are given in Table 13.1. Given the climatic data for a location, it is best to apply these definitions in a certain sequence. The most logical approach is to determine the primary classification first, the secondary classification next, and any tertiary classifications last.

To determine the primary classification, the following questions should be asked in the order given:

Is it an **E** climate?
If not, is it a **B** climate?
If not, is it an **A, C,** or **D** climate?

The first *yes* answer provides the primary classification. The data are then evaluated to arrive at a secondary classification and any tertiary designations.

TABLE 13.1 Köppen Climate-Classification System.

Primary	Secondary	Tertiary	Climatic Characteristics
	Symbol		
A			Tropical Average temperature of the coldest month is above 64.4°F (18°C).
	f		Rainy. Every month has an average rainfall of at least 2.4 in. (6 cm).
	m		Monsoon. Less than 2.4 in. (6 cm) of rainfall in the driest month. **Am** is like **Af** in total rainfall but like **Aw** in its seasonal distribution. See below.
	w		Wet and dry. Distinct dry season in the winter.
			The separation of **Am** and **Aw** climates is found by comparing the rainfall of the driest month (p) with a value determined by the formula: $3.94 - r/25$ (where r is the total annual rainfall).
			If $p > 3.94 - r/25$, then the climate is **Am.** If $p \le 3.94 - r/25$, then the climate is **AW.**
	s		Wet and dry. Well-defined dry season in the summer (rare).
		'	Rainfall maximum shifted to the autumn. Normally applied to an **Aw** climate (yielding the designation **Aw'**).
		"	Two distinct rainfall maxima separated by two dry seasons. Normally applied to an **Aw** climate (yielding the designation **Aw"**).
		g	Ganges-type. Hottest month occurs before the summer solstice and the rainy season.
		i	Isothermal type. Annual range of monthly mean temperatures is less than 9°F (5°C).
		t'	Warmest month is shifted to the autumn (rare).

TABLE 13.1 (continued)

Symbol			
Primary	Secondary	Tertiary	Climatic Characterizations
B			Dry. The rate of evaporation exceeds precipitation. The separation of dry (**B**) climates from humid (**A**, **C**, or **D** climates) is determined by comparing the annual precipitation (*r*) to a value determined by the appropriate formula below. If the annual precipitation (*r*) is less than the amount derived from the appropriate formula, then the climate is a dry (**B**) climate. (If not, it is a humid (**A**, **C**, or **D**) climate.

It is a dry (**B**) climate if:

$r < 0.44t - 8.5$ when the rainfall is evenly distributed throughout the year (neither six-month season has as much as 70% of the total rainfall).

$r < 0.44t - 3$ when more than 70% of the rainfall occurs in the six summer months.

$r < 0.44t - 14$ when 70% or more of the rainfall occurs in the six winter months.

Seasons are defined as April–September and October–March, and t is the annual average temperature.[1]

Symbol			
	S		Semiarid.
	W		Arid.

Separation of the **BS** climate from the **BW** climate is found by dividing the applicable formula given above (see explanation of **B**) by 2. If annual precipitation is less than half the amount given in the definition of **B**, a climate is **BW**. If annual precipitation is more than half the amount given in the definition of **B** (but less than needed for a humid climate), a climate is **BS**.

Example: A place has a total annual rainfall (*r*) of 20 in., gets 70% of this rainfall in the six summer months, and has an average annual temperature (*t*) of 80°F. This place will be classified as having a B climate because

$0.44(80) - 3 = 32.2$,

and 20 (this location's *r*) is less than 32.2. It will be classified as having a BS climate (semiarid) because

$32.2/2 = 16.1$,

and 20 is greater than this amount.

Symbol			
		h	Hot. Annual average temperature is 64.4° F (18°C) or higher. (Low-latitude steppes and deserts.)
		k	Cold. Annual average temperature is less than 64.4° F (18°C). (Middle-latitude steppes, prairies, and deserts.)
		s	Winter rainfall, summer dry season (at least 70% of *r* in the six winter months).
		w	Summer rainfall, winter dry season (at least 70% of *r* in the six summer months).
		n	Frequent occurrence of fog (some coastal dry regions).

[1]An alternate method of determining seasonal distribution of rainfall is as follows: It is *summer rainy* if at least three times as much rain falls in the wettest summer month as in the driest winter month. It is *winter rainy* if at least three times as much rain falls in the wettest winter month as in the driest summer month. There is even distribution if neither of these conditions is met.

TABLE 13.1 (continued)

Primary	Secondary	Tertiary	Climatic Characteristics
	Symbol		
C			Moist, mild winter. Average temperature of the coldest month is below 64.4°F (18°C) but above 26.6°F (−3°C).
	f		Moist, no distinct dry season. Precipitation is evenly distributed and does not satisfy the conditions for a w or s (see below).
	w		Summer rainy, winter dry. More than 70% of precipitation is in the six summer months.
	s		Winter rainy, summer dry. At least 70% of annual precipitation is in the six winter months.
		a	Hot summer. Average temperature of the warmest month is 71.6°F (22°C) or higher, with at least four months 50°F (10°C) or higher.
		b	Cool summer. Average temperature of the warmest month is under 71.6°F (22°C); at least four months with averages of 50°F (10°C) or higher.
		c	Cool, short summer. Average temperature of the warmest month is under 71.6°F; one to three months with averages of 50°F (10°C) or higher.
		x	Precipitation maximum occurs in late spring or early summer, with the summer becoming drier.
		g	Ganges-type. Hottest month occurs before the summer solstice.
		i	Isothermal type. Annual range of mean monthly temperatures is less than 9°F (5°C).
		t′	Warmest month is shifted to the autumn.
D			Humid continental and subarctic. Average temperature of the coldest month is below 26.6°F (−3°C), with the warmest month 50°F (10°C) or higher.
	f		Same as for **C** climates.
	w		Same as for **C** climates.
	s		Same as for **C** climates.
		a	Same as for **C** climates if no month is below −36.4°F (−38°C).
		b	Same as for **C** climates if no month is below −36.4°F (−38°C).
		c	Same as for **C** climates if no month is below −36.4°F (−38°C).
		d	Average temperature of the coldest month is below −36.4°F (−38°C). Whenever **d** can be used, **a, b,** or **c** cannot be used.
E			Polar. Average temperature of the warmest month is below 50°F (10°C).
	T		Tundra. Average temperature of the warmest month is grater than 32°F (0°C) and less than 50°F (10°C).
	F		Icecap. Average temperature of all months is 32°F (0°C) or below.

HOW TO MAKE YOUR OWN KÖPPEN CLASSIFICATION CHARTS

Why bother to calculate the boundary values each and every time data need to be classified? If a few examples of each possible boundary are calculated and plotted on a graph, lines may then be drawn on the graph that will depict the boundaries between the climates involved. This must be done for each of the three possible precipitation regimes (summer, winter, and even distributions). For each of these three situations, the boundary line should be determined between the dry (**B**) and humid (**A, C, D**) climates and another boundary line determined to separate the semiarid (**BS**) from the arid (**BW**) climates. These three graphs will each have two boundary lines that will provide three climate sectors on each graph.

How to Proceed

Using the formula for the boundary between dry and humid climates, when the precipitation is *evenly* distributed, select two or more temperature values (such as 100°F and 40°F) and calculate the value of *r*. Plot these values very *accurately* on the graph in Figure 13.1(a). Connect these points with a straight line (*accurately* drawn) that will extend from one side of the graph to the other side. Next, divide the values of *r* by 2 to find the boundary between the **BS** and **BW** climates (for the same temperatures). Plot these values very carefully on the *same* graph, and again draw a straight line from one edge of the graph to the other that will connect these points. Now label the three sectors that appear on the graph: one sector each for **BW** climates, **BS** climates, and **A, C, D** climates.

Repeat the entire process, but use the formula for *summer* precipitation. Plot the values and draw the lines on the graph for summer precipitation in Figure 13.1(b). Label the three graph sectors with Köppen symbols. Repeat the entire process again using the formula for *winter* precipitation. Using the graph in Figure 13.1(c), carefully plot the values, draw the lines, and label the graph sectors.

You now have three graphs completed. One more graph should be prepared to separate the three tropical climates (**Af, Am, Aw**). On the graph in Figure 13.1(d), draw a *vertical* line at the value of 2.4 in. of rainfall in the driest month. Label the right-hand sector **Af**. Using the formula for finding the boundary between **Am** and **Aw** climates, select at least two possible values for average *annual* rainfall (such as 90 in. and 40 in.), and calculate the **Am–Aw** boundary values. Plot these values on the graph and draw a straight line that will connect these points and extend from the left side of the graph to the vertical line on the right side. Label the **Am** and **Aw** sectors of the graph.

If you have made your calculations without error, and plotted the values and drawn the sector lines accurately, you may now use these graphs to correctly classify thousands of climate stations using the Köppen system. Ninety-five percent of the applicable situations no longer need to be individually computed by formula. Only in a few rare cases, where the data seem to fall *directly* on a sector line, should the calculation be made to provide a precise classification. Even then it is not precise, because such locations represent threshold situations that are transitional between climatic types.

The preparation of these graphs is a significant exercise in itself. However, this exercise is intentionally unnumbered, and the graphs should be considered as a part of the chapter text and remain with it. Before you use your graphs to classify data in the numbered exercises that follow, be sure to have your graphs checked and verified.

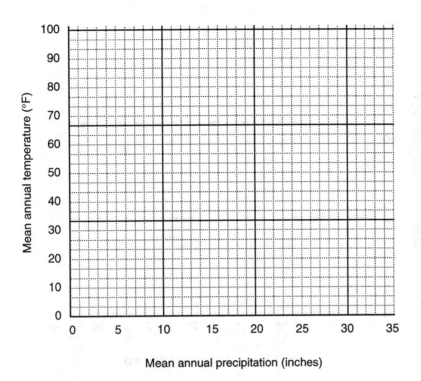

(a) EVEN DISTRIBUTION OF PRECIPITATION

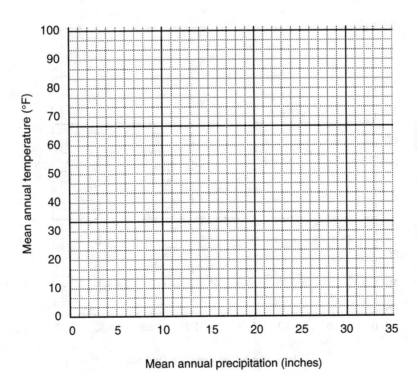

(b) SUMMER CONCENTRATION OF PRECIPITATION

FIGURE 13.1
Köppen Classification Sector Graphs

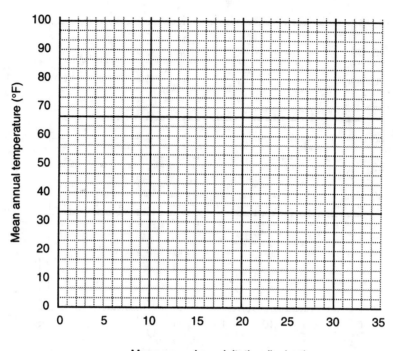

Mean annual precipitation (inches)

(c) WINTER CONCENTRATION OF PRECIPITATION

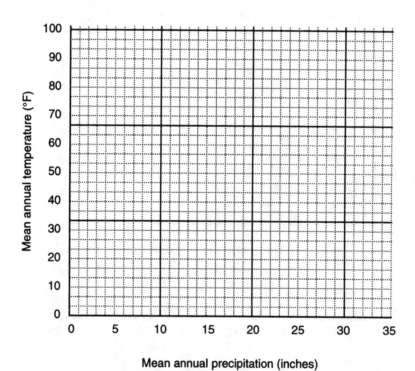

Mean annual precipitation (inches)

(d) TROPICAL CLIMATE BOUNDARIES (Af-Am-Aw)

FIGURE 13.1 *(Continued)*
Köppen Classification Sector Graphs

name   section   date

Exercises

13.1 Classify the climates of the following stations using the Köppen system, and then match each classified station to its location from the list of stations below. Temperatures (T) are averages in degrees Fahrenheit; precipitation figures (P) are averages in inches.

		Jan	Feb	Mar	Apr	May	Jun	Jul	Aug	Sep	Oct	Nov	Dec	Year
1	T	30	32	39	47	56	66	72	71	62	50	39	33	50
	P	0.3	0.6	1.3	2.1	2.0	1.3	1.6	1.5	1.2	1.0	0.6	0.7	14.2
2	T	78	79	80	81	82	81	81	81	80	80	79	79	80
	P	8.5	6.1	6.5	6.9	7.2	6.7	6.8	8.5	7.1	8.2	10.0	10.4	92.9
3	T	56	57	60	65	71	75	77	78	76	73	67	59	68
	P	2.7	1.6	0.8	0.2	0.1	0.0	0.0	0.0	0.1	0.7	1.8	2.6	10.5
4	T	−8	−9	−6	6	25	35	41	41	33	25	14	1	16
	P	0.4	0.5	0.7	0.6	0.6	0.5	0.9	1.1	1.1	1.1	1.1	0.5	9.1
5	T	24	28	40	51	62	71	75	73	65	53	39	28	51
	P	1.8	2.0	2.7	3.3	3.9	3.8	3.8	3.2	3.8	2.4	2.4	2.0	34.9
6	T	45	47	56	65	73	81	84	83	77	66	55	47	65
	P	2.2	2.0	2.7	3.9	4.4	3.1	2.5	2.1	2.9	2.8	2.5	2.4	33.6

	Station 1	Station 2	Station 3	Station 4	Station 5	Station 6
Köppen classification:	_____	_____	_____	_____	_____	_____
Temperature range:	_____	_____	_____	_____	_____	_____
Location:	_____	_____	_____	_____	_____	_____

Actual locations of these six climate stations:

Bengazi, Libya (el. 82 ft)   Peoria, Illinois (el. 652 ft)
Dallas, Texas (el. 481 ft)   Singapore, Singapore (el. 8 ft)
Denver, Colorado (el. 5283 ft)   Upernivik, Greenland (el. 62 ft)

13.2 Using the data for Exercise 13.1, answer the following questions:

a. For each station, list your Köppen designation followed by the most appropriate descriptive name for that station's climate (tropical, savanna, tundra, etc.).

	Köppen	**Descriptive name of climate**
Station 1	_____	_____
Station 2	_____	_____
Station 3	_____	_____
Station 4	_____	_____
Station 5	_____	_____
Station 6	_____	_____

b. Which station is isothermal?   _____

c. Which station is most continental?   _____

d. Station 3 and Station 6 are both at about the same latitude and both have about the same annual average temperature. Explain what you think causes the big differences in the patterns of their monthly temperatures during the year.

e. Station 1 and Station 5 are at about the same latitude and both have about the same annual average temperature. What factors explain why Station 1 is somewhat less extreme in temperatures but more extreme in precipitation?

f. Plot these six climate stations on Map 13.1, page 224. Locate the station on the map with a station circle, print the name of the station next to the circle, and write the Köppen designation of the climate close to the station.

name   section   date

13.3 Classify the climates of the following stations using the Köppen system, and then match each classified station to its location from the list of stations below. Temperatures (T) are averages in degrees Fahrenheit; precipitation figures (P) are averages in inches.

		Jan	Feb	Mar	Apr	May	Jun	Jul	Aug	Sep	Oct	Nov	Dec	Year
1	T	46	50	54	58	63	69	73	72	69	62	53	46	60
	P	3.8	2.9	3.0	1.6	0.8	0.1	0.0	0.0	0.2	0.9	2.1	4.0	19.4
2	T	77	79	84	87	84	81	80	80	81	82	80	77	81
	P	0.2	0.2	0.3	1.6	12.0	18.0	21.4	19.9	15.3	6.9	2.8	0.4	99.0
3	T	22	24	32	43	54	63	68	66	60	49	38	27	46
	P	3.8	3.4	3.9	3.2	3.6	3.3	3.5	3.5	3.3	3.7	3.7	3.8	42.7
4	T	55	59	65	70	77	85	91	90	84	72	61	56	72
	P	0.5	0.4	0.3	0.1	0.0	0.0	0.2	0.6	0.3	0.2	0.3	0.4	3.3
5	T	75	77	79	79	82	82	83	83	82	79	76	74	79
	P	5.1	2.6	1.6	1.5	4.1	9.1	9.6	8.5	9.4	11.0	10.2	6.3	79.0
6	T	72	71	69	65	59	54	52	55	59	62	67	70	63
	P	3.6	4.4	4.9	5.4	5.1	4.8	5.0	3.0	2.9	2.9	2.8	2.8	47.7

	Station 1	**Station 2**	**Station 3**	**Station 4**	**Station 5**	**Station 6**
Köppen classification:	_____	_____	_____	_____	_____	_____
Temperature range:	_____	_____	_____	_____	_____	_____
Location:	_____	_____	_____	_____	_____	_____

Actual locations of these six climate stations:

Belmopan, Belize (el. 7 ft)   Sacramento, California (el. 17 ft)
Portland, Maine (el. 43 ft)   Sydney, Australia (el. 138 ft)
Rangoon, Burma (el. 18 ft)   Yuma, Arizona (el. 194 ft)

name   section   date

13.4 Using the data for Exercise 13.3, answer the following questions:

   a. For each station, list your Köppen designation followed by the most appropriate descriptive name for that station's climate (tropical, savanna, tundra, etc.).

	Köppen	**Descriptive name of climate**
Station 1	_____	_____
Station 2	_____	_____
Station 3	_____	_____
Station 4	_____	_____
Station 5	_____	_____
Station 6	_____	_____

   b. Which station has a Ganges-type climate?   _____

   c. Which station is isothermal?   _____

   d. Station 3 has a coastal location, yet it seems to have a continental temperature range. Why are the winters so cold at Station 3 in spite of its coastal location?

   e. Station 2 and Station 5 are in about the same latitude, they have about the same annual average temperature, and they have heavy annual average precipitation. Station 2 has 25% *more total* precipitation, yet it has 85% *less winter* precipitation during the months of November through March. Explain why this is so.

   f. In determining the location of Station 6, 50% of the earth's surface may be eliminated by a casual glance at the data. What fact should you recognize immediately?

   g. Using Map 13.1 (the same map you used in Exercise 13.2), plot these six climate stations. Locate the station on the map with a station circle, print the name of the station next to the circle, and write the Köppen designation of the climate close to the station.

name   section   date

13.5 From the climate data in Table 28 in Appendix A, classify each station using the Köppen system, give the descriptive name for each type of climate, and determine the annual range of temperature for each station.

	Köppen classification	Descriptive name of the climate	Temperature range
Austin, Texas	_____	_____	_____
Evansville, Indiana	_____	_____	_____
Fargo, North Dakota	_____	_____	_____
Havana, Cuba	_____	_____	_____
Haverhill, Massachusetts	_____	_____	_____
Jacksonville, Florida	_____	_____	_____
Juneau, Alaska	_____	_____	_____
Lima, Peru	_____	_____	_____
Moscow, Russia	_____	_____	_____
New York, New York	_____	_____	_____
Quito, Ecuador	_____	_____	_____
Seattle, Washington	_____	_____	_____
Verkhoyansk, Russia	_____	_____	_____
Cherrapunji, India	_____	_____	_____
Bergen, Norway	_____	_____	_____

13.6 Using Map 13.1 (the same map used in Exercises 13.2 and 13.4), plot these 15 climate stations. Locate each station on the map with a station circle, print the name of the station next to the circle, and write the Köppen designation of the climate close to the station.

13.7 Using the same data used for Exercises 13.5 and 13.6 (Table 28 in Appendix A), answer the following questions:

a. What factors cause the unusual heavy precipitation during the summer at Cherrapunji, India?

b. What climatic control determines the uniformity of temperature throughout the year at Quito, Ecuador?

c. Haverhill, Massachusetts (42° 46′ N) is more than 1000 miles farther south than Juneau, Alaska (58° 18′ N). What reasons account for their winter temperatures being almost identical, even warmer in February at Juneau than at Haverhill?

d. What other climate station in the list of 12 is most similar to Juneau, and what do their locations have in common.

e. What station is most continental?   _____

f. Name three other stations among the twelve that
also appear strongly continental.   _____

                                                            _____

                                                            _____

g. Why are two of the three stations (from your above answer) continental in climate even though they are located very close to a large ocean?

h. Which station in the list of twelve is truly isothermal?

i. Give *three* different reasons why a station may have an isothermal climate.

j. Explain why Verkhoyansk, Russia, should *not* be considered a desert even though it averages only 5.3 in. (13.5 cm) of precipitation per year.

name   section   date

In doing exercises 13.8 *to* 13.18, *you may consult any good map of world climate regions.* Just about every textbook in meteorology, climatology, geography (especially physical geography), weather and climate, etc., has such a map. The map you use does not have to be a Köppen map. Other maps will indicate regions that are very close to the Köppen regionalization. Differences in terminology and boundary positions are usually minor at the scale we are concerned with.

13.8   What are the names of the climates with boundaries that seem to approximate the 20-in. (50-cm) isohyet?

13.9   Tropical wet climates (tropical rain forest and tropical monsoon climates) are just about always bordered by only one type of climate. What is this bordering climate, and why does it always border the very wet tropical climates?

13.10   Imagine taking a long cruise along the coast from northern Alaska all the way to the southern tip of South America. *List* each type of climate you will find along the coast, from north to south, as you make this journey.

13.11   Take another excursion, but this time travel along the coast of western Europe and western Africa. You start in northern Norway and travel the coast of Europe and then Africa all the way to the Cape of Good Hope in South Africa. *List* each type of climate you will find along the way.

name   section   date

13.12 Compare the lists in Exercises 13.10 and 13.11. What generalization can you make about the two west-coast climate sequences?

13.13 Take another coastal journey along the east coast of North America from northeastern Canada to southern Florida. *List* the climates you will find along the coast as you travel south.

13.14 Take one more coastal journey. This time, travel from northeastern Siberia southward to southern China. *List* the climates you will find along the coast.

13.15 Compare the lists of your east coast trips in Exercises 13.13 and 13.14. What generalization can you make about the two east-coast sequences of climates?

13.16 Study the several areas in the world that have a Mediterranean climate. What is it about their *locations* that all Mediterranean climates have in common?

name   section   date

13.17 Study the several areas in the world that have a marine west coast climate. What is it about their *locations* that all marine west coast climates have in common?

13.18 On the map of the world, Map 13.3, draw in the boundaries as accurately as possible of the major climate regions (the boundaries between the **A, B, C, D,** and **E** climates). Within the areas of the **B** climates, print the names of the following major deserts:

Mojave	Rub Al Khali
Great Salt Lake	Persian
Baja	Gobi
Sonora	Turkestanian
Peruvian	Negev
Atacama	Great Sandy
Patagonian	Gibson
Namib	Great Victoria
Kalahari	Simpson
Sahara	Thar
Libyan	

name   section   date

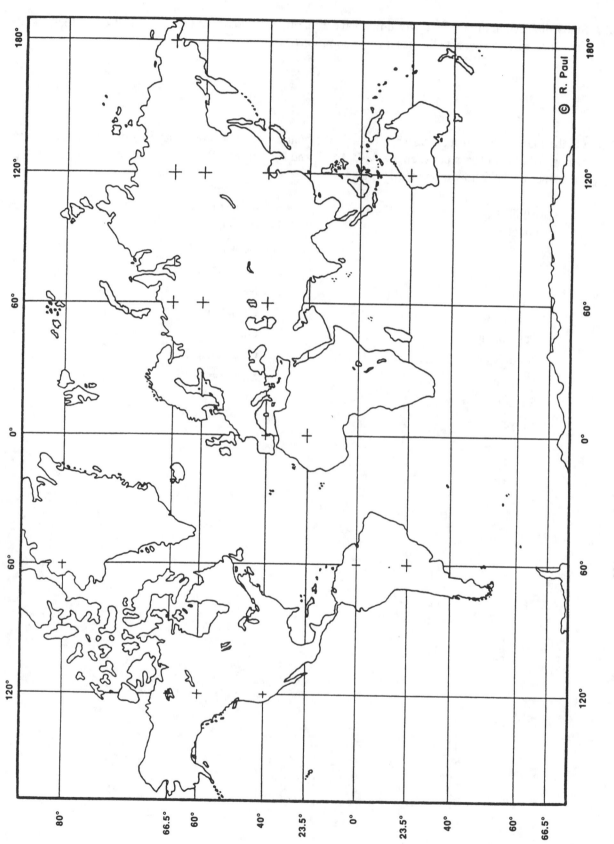

Map 13.1 (For Exercises 13.2, 13.4, and 13.6)

© R. Paul

name   section   date

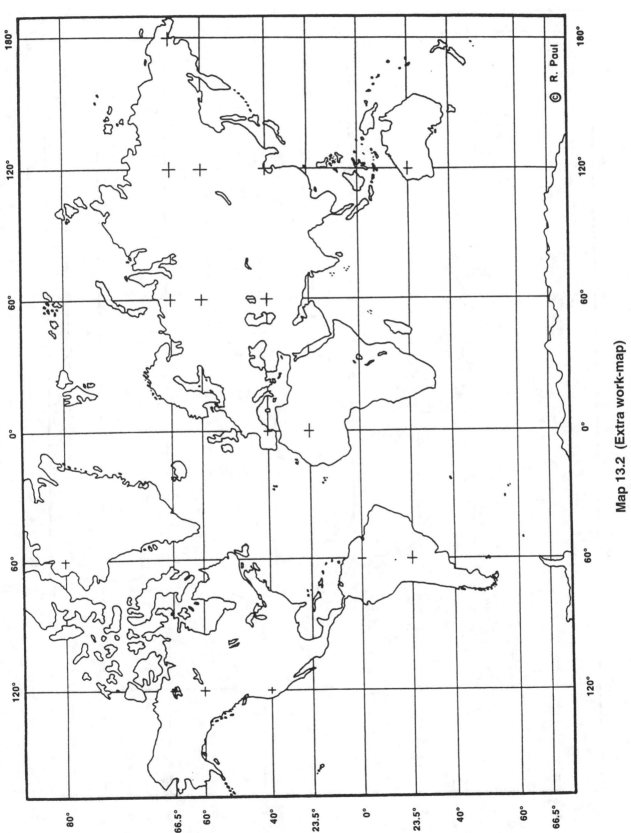

Map 13.2 (Extra work-map)

© R. Paul

name   section   date

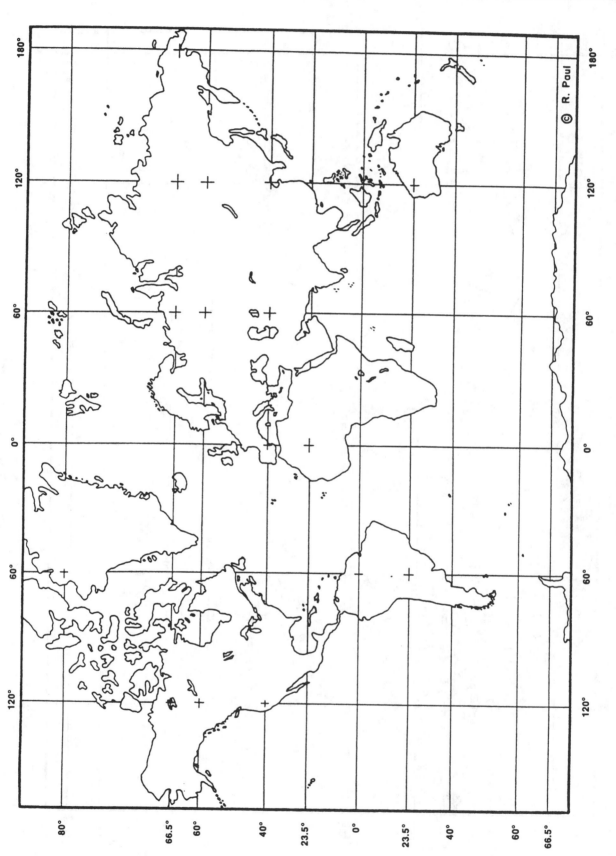

Map 13.3 (For Exercise 13.18.)

© R. Paul

name   section   date
_____

Review and Study Questions

1. How are *weather* and *climate* similar and in what ways are they different?

2. If a region is considered to have a year-round "hot and dry" climate, which *climatic controls* probably dominate that region?

3. Many possible causes for long-term changes in climate have been suggested. Identify some of these possible causes.

4. Explain how climate and vegetation are related.

5. Explain how climate and soils are related.

6. Describe how vertical climatic zones within some mountainous regions compare with the basic latitudinal distribution of climates closer to sea level.

7. Write a concise statement describing what factors (climate elements) are used, and in what order, to classify a location using the Köppen system.

8. In what ways might the climate of a large city be different from its surrounding rural area?

9. The many climatic classifications that have been developed tend to be either statistical or genetic in nature. Statistical classifications like the Köppen system (and the Thornthwaite system) are based heavily on temperature and precipitation data. Genetic classifications are based more on the causes of climates. What factors or causes do you think might be used as a basis for a genetic classification of climates?

appendix **A** ——————————————————————
TABLES

Table 1
SI (Système Internationale) Units

SI Base Units

Physical Quantity	Name of Unit	Symbol
length	meter	m
mass	kilogram	kg
time	second	s
electric current	ampere	A
thermodynamic temperature	kelvin	K
amount of substance	mole	mol

Prefixes for Fractions and Multiples of SI Units

Fraction	Prefix	Symbol	Multiple	Prefix	Symbol
10^{-1}	deci	d	10	deka	da
10^{-2}	centi	c	10^2	hecto	h
10^{-3}	milli	m	10^3	kilo	k
10^{-6}	micro	μ	10^6	mega	M
10^{-9}	nano	n	10^9	giga	G
10^{-12}	pico	p	10^{12}	tera	T
10^{-15}	femto	f			
10^{-18}	atto	a			

Note: Multiple prefixes, such as μμF for pF, should not be used.

Special Names and Symbols for Certain SI-Derived Units

Physical Quantity	Name of Si Unit	Symbol for SI Unit	Definition of Unit
force	newton	N	$kg\ m\ s^{-2}$
pressure	pascal	Pa	$kg\ m^{-1}\ s^{-2}(N= m^{-2})$
energy	joule	J	$kg\ m^2\ s^{-2}$
power	watt	W	$kg\ m^2\ s^{-3}\ (=J\ s^{-1})$
electric charge	coulomb	C	$A\ s$
electric potential difference	volt	V	$kg\ m^2\ s^{-3}\ A{-}1\ (= J\ A^{-1}\ s^{-1})$
frequency	hertz	Hz	s^{-1}(cycle per second)

Decimal Fractions and Multiples of SI Units Having Special Names

Physical Quantity	Name of Unit	Symbol for Unit	Definition of Unit
length	ångström	Å	$10^{-10}\ m = 10^{-8}\ cm$
length	micrometer*	μm	$10^{-6}\ m = μm$*
force	dyne	dyn	$10^{-5}\ N$
pressure	bar	bar	$10^5\ N\ m^{-2}$
energy	erg	erg	$10^{-7}\ J$

*The word micron and the symbol μ have been replaced by micrometer and the symbol μm.

Table 2
Conversion Factors for Commonly Used Units

Length	Å	in.	m	cm
1 ångstrom (Å)	1	3.92×10^{-9}	10^{-10}	10^{-8}
1 inch (in.)	2.54×10^{8}	1	2.54×10^{-2}	2.54
1 meter (m)	10^{10}	39.37	1	10^{2}
1 centimeter (cm)	10^{8}	.3937	10^{-2}	1

Mass	lb	oz	kg	g
1 pound (lb)	1	32	.4536	453.6
1 ounce (oz)	.0625	1	2.836×10^{-2}	28.36
1 kilogram (kg)	2.204	35.3	1	1000
1 gram (g)	2.204×10^{-3}	.0353	.001	1

Pressure	atm	Pa	mm Hg	dyn cm^{-2}	lb. in.$^{-2}$
1 atmosphere (atm)	1	1.013×10^{5}	760	1.013	14.70
1 pascal (Pa)	9.872×10^{-6}	1	7.502×10^{-3}	10^{-5}	1.451×10^{-4}
1 torr (mm Hg)	1.32×10^{-3}	1.333×10^{2}	1	1.33×10^{-5}	1.93×10^{-2}
1 bar (dyn cm–2)	9.872×10^{-1}	10^{5}	7.502×10^{2}	1	1.451×10^{1}
1 pound per square inch (lb in.–2)	6.803×10^{-2}	6.891×10^{3}	$5.17\ 10^{1}$	6.891×10^{-2}	1

Temperature	°K	°F	°C
1 degree Kelvin (°K)	1	9/5(°K) – 459.7	°K + 273.16*
1 degree Fahrenheit (°F)	5/9(°F) + 255.4	1	5/9 (°F – 32)
1 degree Celcius (°C)	°C – 273	9/5(°C) + 32	1

Energy	J	erg	cal	kWh
1 joule (J)	1	10^{7}	.2390	2.8×10^{-7}
1 erg (erg)	10^{-7}	1	2.390×10^{-8}	2.8×10^{-14}
1 thermochemical calorie (cal)	4.184	4.184×10^{7}	1	1.162×10^{-6}
1 kilowatt-hour (kWh)	3.6×10^{6}	3.6×10^{13}	8.604×10^{5}	1

Volume	ml	cm3	qt	oz
1 milliliter (ml)	1	1	1.06×10^{-3}	3.392×10^{-2}
1 cubic centimeter (cm3)	1	1	1.06×10^{-3}	3.392×10^{-2}
1 quart (qt)	943	943	1	32
1 fluid ounce (oz)	29.5	29.5	3.125×10^{-2}	1

*Absolute zero (°K) = –273.16 °C.

Table 3
Trigonometric Functions

Angle Degrees	Sine	Cosine	Tangent	Angle Degrees	Sine	Cosine	Tangent
0	.0000	1.0000	.0000	46	.7193	.6947	1.0355
1	.0175	.9999	.0175	47	.7314	.6820	1.0724
2	.0349	.9994	.0349	48	.7431	.6691	1.1106
3	.0523	.9986	.0524	49	.7547	.6561	1.1504
4	.0698	.9976	.0699	50	.7660	.6428	1.1918
5	.0872	.9962	.0875	51	.7772	.6293	1.2349
6	.1045	.9945	.1051	52	.7880	.6157	1.2799
7	.1219	.9926	.1228	53	.7986	.6018	1.3270
8	.1392	.9903	.1405	54	.8090	.5878	1.3764
9	.1564	.9877	.1584	55	.8192	.5736	1.4281
10	.1737	.9848	.1763	56	.8290	.5592	1.4826
11	.1908	.9816	.1944	57	.8387	.5446	1.5399
12	.2079	.9782	.2126	58	.8481	.5299	1.6003
13	.2250	.9744	.2309	59	.8572	.5150	1.6643
14	.2419	.9703	.2493	60	.8660	.5000	1.7321
15	.2588	.9659	.2680	61	.8746	.4848	1.8040
16	.2756	.9613	.2868	62	.8830	.4695	1.8807
17	.2924	.9563	.3057	63	.8910	.4540	1.9626
18	.3090	.9511	.3249	64	.8988	.4384	2.0503
19	.3256	.9455	.3443	65	.9063	.4226	2.1445
20	.3420	.9397	.3640	66	.9136	.4067	2.2460
21	.3584	.9336	.3839	67	.9205	.3907	2.3559
22	.3746	.9272	.4040	68	.9272	.3746	2.4751
23	.3907	.9205	.4245	69	.9336	.3584	2.6051
24	.4067	.9136	.4452	70	.9397	.3420	2.7475
25	.4226	.9063	.4663	71	.9455	.3256	2.9042
26	.4384	.8988	.4877	72	.9511	.3090	3.0777
27	.4540	.8910	.5095	73	.9563	.2924	3.2709
28	.4695	.8830	.5317	74	.9613	.2756	3.4874
29	.4848	.8746	.5543	75	.9659	.2588	3.7321
30	.5000	.8660	.5774	76	.9703	.2419	4.0108
31	.5150	.8572	.6009	77	.9744	.2250	4.3315
32	.5299	.8481	.6249	78	.9782	.2079	4.7046
33	.5446	.8387	.6494	79	.9816	.1908	5.1446
34	.5592	.8290	.6745	80	.9848	.1737	5.6713
35	.5736	.8192	.7002	81	.9877	.1564	6.3138
36	.5878	.8090	.7265	82	.9903	.1392	7.1154
37	.6018	.7986	.7536	83	.9926	.1219	8.1443
38	.6157	.7880	.7813	84	.9945	.1045	9.5144
39	.6293	.7772	.8098	85	.9962	.0872	11.430
40	.6428	.7660	.8391	86	.9976	.0698	14.301
41	.6561	.7547	.8693	87	.9986	.0523	19.081
42	.6691	.7431	.9004	88	.9994	.0349	28.636
43	.6820	.7314	.9325	89	.9999	.0175	57.290
44	.6947	.7193	.9657	90	1.0000	.0000	——
45	.7071	.7071	1.0000				

Table 4
Squares and Square Roots

x	x²	√x	x	x²	√x
1	1	1.000	51	2601	7.141
2	4	1.414	52	2704	7.211
3	9	1.732	53	2809	7.280
4	16	2.000	54	2916	7.349
5	25	2.236	55	3025	7.416
6	36	2.449	56	3136	7.483
7	49	2.646	57	3249	7.550
8	64	2.828	58	3364	7.616
9	81	3.000	59	3481	7.681
10	100	3.162	60	3600	7.746
11	121	3.317	61	3721	7.810
12	144	3.464	62	3844	7.874
13	169	3.606	63	3969	7.937
14	196	3.742	64	4096	8.000
15	225	3.873	65	4225	8.062
16	256	4.000	66	4356	8.124
17	289	4.123	67	4489	8.185
18	324	4.243	68	4624	8.246
19	361	4.359	69	4761	8.307
20	400	4.472	70	4900	8.367
21	441	4.583	71	5041	8.426
22	484	4.690	72	5184	8.485
23	529	4.796	73	5329	8.544
24	576	4.899	74	5476	8.602
25	625	5.000	75	5625	8.660
26	676	5.099	76	5776	8.718
27	729	5.196	77	5929	8.775
28	784	5.292	78	6084	8.832
29	841	5.385	79	6241	8.888
30	900	5.477	80	6400	8.944
31	961	5.568	81	6561	9.000
32	1024	5.657	82	6724	9.055
33	1089	5.745	83	6889	9.110
34	1156	5.831	84	7056	9.165
35	1225	5.916	85	7225	9.220
36	1296	6.000	86	7396	9.274
37	1369	6.083	87	7569	9.327
38	1444	6.164	88	7744	9.381
39	1521	6.245	89	7921	9.434
40	1600	6.325	90	8100	9.487
41	1681	6.403	91	8281	9.539
42	1764	6.481	92	8464	9.592
43	1849	6.557	93	8649	9.644
44	1936	6.633	94	8836	9.695
45	2025	6.708	95	9025	9.747
46	2116	6.782	96	9216	9.798
47	2209	6.856	97	9409	9.849
48	2304	6.928	98	9604	9.899
49	2401	7.000	99	9801	9.950
50	2500	7.071	100	10000	10.000

Table 5
Nautical Miles, Statute Miles, and Kilometers

Nautical Miles	Statute Miles	Kilometers
1	1.15	1.85
2	2.30	3.70
3	3.45	5.56
4	4.60	7.41
5	5.75	9.26
6	6.90	11.12
7	8.06	12.96
8	9.21	14.82
9	10.36	16.67
10	11.51	18.52
20	23.02	37.04
30	34.52	55.56
40	46.03	74.08
50	57.54	92.60
60	69.05	111.12
70	80.55	129.64
80	92.06	148.16
90	103.57	166.68
100	115.08	185.20
200	230.16	370.40
300	345.03	555.60
400	460.31	740.80
500	575.39	926.00
600	690.47	1111.20
700	805.55	1296.40
800	920.62	1481.60
900	1035.70	1666.80
1000	1150.78	1852.00

1 nautical mile (international)	=	6076.12	feet
		1.151	statute miles
		1852.000	meters
		1.852	kilometer

1 statute mile	=	5280.000	feet
		.869	nautical mile
		1609.345	meters
		1.609	kilometer

1 kilometer	=	3280.65	feet
		.54	nautical mile
		.62	statute mile
		1000.00	meters

See Table 16 for wind speed conversions.

Table 6
Length of the Daylight Period

The *daylight period* is defined as the time between sunrise and sunset, each of which occurs when the upper edge of the disk of the sun is exactly on the horizon. *Civil twilight* lengthens this period because it is measured from the time when the center of the sun is 6 degrees below the horizon (when first-magnitude stars are just visible). *Astronomical twilight* lengthens the daylight period still more, since it is defined by the center of the sun being 18 degrees below the horizon (when stars of the sixth magnitude are visible with no trace of twilight glow on the horizon). The table that follows presents the *traditional* values for the daylight period. Actually, the equator normally has about 12 hr 7 min of daylight throughout the year. The length of the daylight period at the equinoxes varies by latitude from 12 hr 7 min at the equator to 12 hr 23 min at 60 degrees N or S and longer at the poles. The continuous daylight or darkness periods vary also. At 70 degrees N the values are 2 months and about 10 days of light, 1 month and about 20 days of darkness. At 80 degrees N the periods are 4 months and about 20 days of light, 4 months and about 5 days of darkness. At 90 degrees N, the values are 6 months and about 12 days of light, 5 months and about 25 days of darkness. At these high latitudes the data are increasingly uncertain because of the large variation in daylight resulting from small changes in atmospheric refraction. Clearly, there are more days of continuous daylight and fewer days with no daylight in the Arctic region than in the Antarctic region. At the North Pole there are about nine days more with continuous daylight and about nine days fewer with no daylight than at the South Pole.

Latitude	Winter Solstice		Summer Solstice		Equinoxes	
0°	12 hr	0 min	12 hr	0 min	12 hr	0 min
10°	11	25	12	35	12	0
20°	10	48	13	12	12	0
30°	10	4	13	56	12	0
40°	9	8	14	52	12	0
50°	7	42	16	18	12	0
60°	5	33	18	27	12	0
70°	0	0	2 months		12	0
80°	0	0	4 months		12	0
90°	0	0	6 months		12	0

Table 7
Pressure and Density in the Atmosphere

Height (m)	Pressure (mb)	Density (kg/m3)
0	1013.25	1.2250
100	1001.20	1.2133
200	989.45	1.2017
300	977.72	1.1901
400	966.11	1.1786
500	954.60	1.1673
600	943.21	1.1560
700	931.93	1.1448
800	920.76	1.1336
900	909.70	1.1226
1000	898.74	1.1116
2000	794.95	1.0065
3000	701.08	.90912
4000	616.40	.81913
5000	540.19	.73612
6000	471.81	.65970
7000	410.60	.58950
8000	355.99	.52517
9000	307.42	.46635
10,000	264.36	.41271
20,000	54.748	.088035
30,000	11.718	.01812
40,000	2.7752	.0038510
50,000	.75944	.00097752
60,000	.20314	.00028832
70,000	.046342	.000074243
80,000	.0088627	.000015701

Table 8
Standard Pressure Heights

Standard Pressure Surface	Approximate Height Above Sea Level	
	Meters	Feet
1013 mb	Sea level	Sea level
1000 mb	120	400
850 mb	1500	5000
700 mb	3000	10,000
500 mb	5500	18,000
400 mb	7200	23,500
300 mb	9000	30,000
200 mb	12,000	39,000
100 mb	16,000	53,000
50 mb	20,500	67,500
10 mb	30,800	102,000

Table 9
Relative Humidity (in Percent)

Appendix A   Tables

Depression of Wet-Bulb Thermometer (°F)

Air Temperature °F	1	2	3	4	5	6	7	8	9	10	11	12	13	14	15	16	17	18	19	20	21	22	23	24	25	26	27	28	29	30	31	32	33	34	35
0	67	33	1																																
5	73	46	20																																
10	78	56	34	13																															
15	82	64	46	29	11																														
20	85	70	55	40	26	12																													
25	87	74	62	49	37	25	13	1																											
30	89	78	67	56	46	36	26	16	6																										
35	91	81	72	63	54	45	36	27	19	10	2																								
40	92	83	75	68	60	52	45	37	29	22	15	7																							
45	93	86	78	71	64	57	51	44	38	31	25	18	12	6																					
50	93	87	81	74	68	61	55	49	43	38	32	27	21	16	10	5																			
55	94	88	82	76	70	65	59	54	49	43	38	33	28	23	19	11																			
60	94	89	83	78	73	68	63	58	53	48	43	39	34	30	26	21	17	13	9																
65	95	90	85	80	75	70	66	61	56	52	48	43	39	35	31	27	24	20	16	12	9	6	3												
70	95	90	86	81	77	72	68	64	59	55	51	48	44	40	36	33	29	25	22	18	15	12	9	6	3										
75	96	91	86	82	78	74	70	66	62	58	54	51	47	44	40	37	34	30	27	24	21	18	15	12	9	7	4	1							
80	96	91	87	83	79	75	72	68	64	61	57	54	50	47	44	41	38	35	32	29	26	23	20	18	15	12	10	7	5	3					
85	96	92	88	84	81	77	73	70	66	63	59	56	53	50	47	44	41	38	36	33	30	27	25	22	20	17	15	13	10	8	6	4	2		
90	96	92	89	85	82	78	74	71	68	65	61	58	55	52	49	47	44	41	39	36	34	31	29	26	24	22	19	17	15	13	11	9	7	5	3
95	96	93	89	85	82	79	76	73	69	66	63	60	58	55	52	50	47	44	42	39	37	34	32	30	28	25	23	21	19	17	15	13	11	10	8
100	96	93	89	86	83	80	77	73	70	68	65	62	59	56	54	51	49	46	44	41	39	37	35	33	30	28	26	24	22	21	19	17	15	13	12
105	97	93	90	87	84	81	78	75	72	69	66	64	61	58	56	53	51	49	46	44	42	40	38	36	34	32	30	28	26	24	22	21	19	17	15
110	97	93	90	87	84	81	78	75	73	70	67	65	62	60	57	55	52	50	48	46	44	42	40	38	36	34	32	30	28	26	25	23	21	20	18
115	97	94	91	88	85	82	79	76	74	71	69	66	64	61	59	57	54	52	50	48	46	44	42	40	38	36	34	33	31	29	28	26	25	23	21
120	97	94	91	88	85	82	80	77	74	72	69	67	65	62	60	58	55	53	51	49	47	45	43	41	40	38	36	34	33	31	29	28	26	25	23
125	97	94	91	88	86	83	80	78	75	73	70	68	66	64	61	59	57	55	53	51	49	47	45	44	42	40	38	37	35	33	32	30	29	27	26
130	97	94	91	89	86	83	81	78	76	73	71	69	67	64	62	60	58	56	54	52	50	48	47	45	43	41	40	38	37	35	33	32	30	29	28

Table 10
Temperature of Dew Point (Fahrenheit)

Air Temperature (°F)	Vapor Pressure (in.)	Depression of Wet-Bulb Thermometer (°F)																																	
		1	2	3	4	5	6	7	8	9	10	11	12	13	14	15	16	17	18	19	20	21	22	23	24	25	26	27	28	29	30	31	32	33	34	35
0	0.0383	-7	-20																																	
5	0.0491	-1	-9	-24																																
10	0.0631	5	-2	-10	-27																															
15	0.0810	11	6	0	-9	-26																														
20	0.103	16	12	8	2	-7	-21																													
25	0.130	22	19	15	10	5	-3	-15	-51																											
30	0.164	27	25	21	18	14	8	2	-7	-25																										
35	0.203	33	30	28	25	21	17	13	7	0	-11	-41																								
40	0.247	38	35	33	30	28	25	21	18	13	7	-1	-14																							
45	0.298	43	41	38	36	34	31	28	25	22	18	13	7	-1	-14																					
50	0.360	48	46	44	42	40	37	34	32	29	26	22	18	13	8	0	-13																			
55	0.432	53	51	50	48	45	43	41	38	36	33	30	27	24	20	15	9	1	-12	-59																
60	0.517	58	57	55	53	51	49	47	45	43	40	38	35	32	29	25	21	17	11	4	-8	-36														
65	0.616	63	62	60	59	57	55	53	51	49	47	45	42	40	37	34	31	27	24	19	14	7	-3	-22												
70	0.732	69	67	65	64	62	61	59	57	55	53	51	49	47	44	42	39	36	33	30	26	22	17	11	2	-11										
75	0.866	74	72	71	69	68	66	64	63	61	59	57	55	54	51	49	47	44	42	39	36	32	29	25	21	15	8	-2	-23							
80	1.022	79	77	76	74	73	72	70	68	67	65	63	62	60	58	56	54	52	50	47	44	42	39	36	32	28	24	20	13	6	-7	-53				
85	1.201	84	82	81	80	78	77	75	74	72	71	69	68	66	64	62	61	59	57	54	52	50	48	45	42	39	36	32	28	24	19	12	3	-12		
90	1.408	89	87	86	85	83	82	81	79	78	76	75	73	72	70	69	67	65	63	61	59	57	55	53	51	48	45	43	39	36	32	28	24	19	11	1
95	1.645	94	93	91	90	89	87	86	85	83	82	80	79	78	76	74	73	71	70	68	66	64	62	60	58	56	54	52	49	46	43	40	37	33	29	24
100	1.916	99	98	96	95	94	93	91	90	89	87	86	85	83	82	80	79	77	76	74	72	71	69	67	65	63	61	59	57	55	52	50	47	44	41	37
105	2.225	104	103	101	100	99	98	96	95	94	93	91	90	89	87	86	84	83	82	80	78	77	75	74	72	70	68	67	65	63	61	58	56	54	51	48
110	2.576	109	108	106	105	104	103	102	100	99	98	97	95	94	93	91	90	89	87	86	84	83	81	80	78	77	75	73	72	70	68	66	64	62	60	57
115	2.975	114	113	112	110	109	108	107	106	104	103	102	101	99	98	97	96	94	93	92	90	89	87	86	84	83	81	80	78	76	75	73	71	69	67	65
120	2.425	119	118	117	115	114	113	112	111	110	108	107	106	105	104	102	101	100	98	97	96	94	93	92	90	89	87	86	84	83	81	80	78	76	75	73
125	3.933	124	123	122	121	119	118	117	116	115	114	112	111	110	109	108	106	105	104	103	101	100	99	97	96	95	93	92	90	89	88	86	84	83	81	80
130	4.504	129	128	127	126	124	123	122	121	120	119	118	116	115	114	113	112	110	109	108	107	106	104	103	102	100	99	98	96	95	94	92	91	89	88	86

Table 11
Saturation Mixing Ratios (r_w)

°F	g/kg	°F	g/kg	°F	g/kg
0	0.92	35	4.26	70	15.62
5	1.15	40	5.21	75	18.76
10	1.49	45	6.20	80	22.25
15	1.89	50	7.61	85	26.19
20	2.22	55	9.27	90	30.70
25	2.80	60	11.05	95	36.50
30	3.49	65	13.16	100	42.99

Table 12
Saturation Absolute Humidities (d_s)

°F	grains/foot^3	°F	grains/foot^3	°F	grains/foot^3
0	0.479	35	2.375	70	8.066
5	0.613	40	2.863	75	9.460
10	0.780	45	3.436	80	11.056
15	0.988	50	4.108	85	12.878
20	1.244	55	4.891	90	14.951
25	1.558	60	5.800	95	17.305
30	1.942	65	6.852	100	19.901

Table 13
Saturation Absolute Humidities (d_s)

°C	grams/meter^3	°C	grams/meter^3	°C	grams/meter^3
−20	1.1	5	6.8	30	30.5
−15	1.6	10	9.4	35	39.7
−10	2.3	15	12.9	40	51.2
−5	3.4	20	17.3	45	65.6
0	4.8	25	23.2	50	83.0

Note: 1 gram = 15.4324 grains = 0.0352740 ounce = 0.0022046 pound.
   1 grain = 0.0647989 gram = 0.00228571 ounce.
   1 ounce (avoir.) = 437.5 grains = 28.3495 grams.

Table 14
The Radar Summary Chart

Echo Coverage Symbols

Symbol	Meaning	Called
(line symbol)	A line of echoes	Line
(cloud symbol)	An area of echoes	Area
⊕	Over 9/10 coverage	Solid
(broken symbol)	6/10 to 9/10 coverage	Broken
(scattered symbol)	1/10 to 5/10 coverage	Scattered
⊙	Less than 1/10 coverage	Widely scattered
○	Isolated cell (ISOLD)	Cell
●	Strong cell detected by one radar	Cell
✸	Strong cell detected by two or more radars	Cell

Weather Symbols

Symbol	Meaning
R	Rain
RW	Rain showers
A	Hail
S	Snow
IP	Ice Pellets
SW	Snow showers
L	Drizzle
T	Thunderstorm
ZR, ZL	Freezing precipitation

Intensity Trend

Symbol	Meaning
+	Increasing
–	Decreasing
NC	No change
NEW	New

No Echo Notations

Symbol	Meaning
NE	No echo (equipment operating but no echoes observed)
NA	Observation not available
OM	Equipment out for maintenance

Echo Intensities

Symbol	Echo intensity	Estimated precipitation
–	Weak	Light
(none)	Moderate	Moderate
+	Strong	Heavy
++	Very Strong	Very Heavy
X	Intense	Intense
XX	Extreme	Extreme
U	Unknown	Unknown

Examples: Type, Intensity, Trend

Symbol	Meaning
R–/+	Light rain, increasing in intensity.
TRW+/–	Thunderstorm, heavy rain shower, decreasing in intensity.
RW/NC	Moderate rain shower, no change in intensity
TRW–/NEW	Thunderstorm, light rain shower, newly developed.
TRWXX/NC	Thunderstorm, rain shower extreme intensity, no change.
S	Snow. (No intensity or characteristic is shown for frozen precipitation.)
(dashed box)	Severe weather watch in effect.

Cell, Line, or Area Movement

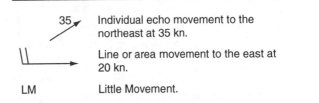

35 (arrow)	Individual echo movement to the northeast at 35 kn.
(line/arrow)	Line or area movement to the east at 20 kn.
LM	Little Movement.

Heights of Echo Bases and Tops

Heights in hundreds of feet MSL are entered above or below a line to denote echo tops and bases respectively. Examples are:

450	Average tops 45,000 ft
220 / 80	Bases 8000 ft; tops 22,000 ft
330	Top of an individual cell, 33,000 ft
\650/	Maximum tops, 65,000 ft
A350	Tops 35,000 ft reported by aircraft

Table 15
Cloud Coverage (N and N_h)

N is for the total cloud cover. N_h is for the clouds reported in h (the fraction of the celestial dome covered by all the C_L present, or if no C_L clouds, the fraction covered by all C_M clouds).

N	N_h	Sky Coverage
○	0	No clouds
◐	1	1/10 or less
◕	2	2/10 and 3/10
◕	3	4/10
◑	4	5/10
⊖	5	6/10
◕	6	7/10 and 8/10
◗	7	9/10 or overcast with openings
●	8	Completely overcast
⊗	9	Sky obscured

Note: On marine radiofacsimile weather maps the following symbols are used for sky coverage:

☐	Clear sky
☐	1/8 to 2/8
☐	3/8 to 5/8
☐	6/8 to 8/8
☒	Sky obscured

Table 16
Wind Speed (ff)

ff Symbol	Knots		Miles per Hour
◯	Less than 1	(Calm)	Less than 1
⎯	1-2		1-2
(barb)	3-7		3-8
(barb)	8-12		9-14
(barb)	13-17		15-20
(barb)	18-22		21-25
(barb)	23-27		26-31
(barb)	28-32		32-37
(barb)	33-37		38-43
(barb)	38-42		44-49
(barb)	43-47		50-54
(pennant)	48-52		55-60
(pennant)	53-57		61-66
(pennant)	58-62		67-71
(pennant)	63-67		72-77
(pennant)	68-72		78-83
(pennant)	73-77		84-89

Incremental values of symbols:

A half flag	=	5 knots.
A whole flag	=	10 knots.
A pennant	=	50 knots.

Some additional conversion factors:

1 knot	=	1 nautical mile per hour
		(1 nautical mile = 6076.12 feet)
		(1 statute mile = 5280 feet)

1 knot	=	1.15155 miles per hour (statute)
1 knot	=	1.854 kilometers per hour (km/hr)
1 knot	=	0.514791 meter per second (m/sec)

1 mile per hour	=	0.868391 knot
1 mile per hour	=	0.44704 meter per second (m/sec)
1 mile per hour	=	1.609344 kilometers per hour (km/hr)

1 kilometer per hour	=	0.539925 knot
1 kilometer per hour	=	0.621335 miles per hour (mi/hr)
1 kilometer per hour	=	0.277778 meter per second (m/sec)

1 meter per second	=	2.23694 miles per hour (mi/hr)
1 meter per second	=	1.943 knots
1 meter per second	=	3.60 kilometers per hour (km/hr)

See Table 5 for Nautical Mile, Statute Mile, and Kilometer conversions.

Table 17
Horizontal Visibility (VV)[1]

Code Figure	Statute Miles	Yards	Kilometers
00	Less than $\frac{1}{16}$	Less than 110.	Less than 0.1.
01	$\frac{1}{16}$	110	0.1
02	$\frac{1}{8}$	220	0.2
03	$\frac{3}{16}$	330	0.3
04	$\frac{1}{4}$	440	0.4
05	$\frac{5}{16}$	550	0.5
06	$\frac{3}{8}$	660	0.6
07	$\frac{7}{16}$	770	0.7
08	$\frac{1}{2}$	880	0.8
09	$\frac{9}{16}$	990	0.9
10	$\frac{5}{8}$	1100	1.0
11	$\frac{11}{16}$	1210	1.1
12	$\frac{3}{4}$	1320	1.2
13	$\frac{13}{16}$	1430	1.3
14	$\frac{7}{8}$	1540	1.4
15	$\frac{15}{16}$	1650	1.5
16	1	1760	1.6
17	$1\frac{1}{16}$	1870	1.7
18	$1\frac{1}{8}$	1980	1.8
19	$1\frac{3}{16}$	2090	1.9
20	$1\frac{1}{4}$	2200	2.0
21	$1\frac{5}{16}$	2310	2.1
22	$1\frac{3}{8}$	2420	2.2
23	$1\frac{7}{16}$	2530	2.3

Code Figure	Statute Miles	Yards	Kilometers
54	Not specified.		
55	Not specified.		
56	$3\frac{3}{4}$	6600	6
57	$4\frac{3}{8}$	7700	7
58	5	etc.	8
59	$5\frac{3}{8}$		9
60	$6\frac{1}{4}$		10
61	$6\frac{7}{8}$		11
62	$7\frac{1}{2}$		12
63	$8\frac{1}{8}$		13
64	$8\frac{3}{4}$		14
65	$9\frac{3}{8}$		15
66	10		16
67	$10\frac{5}{8}$		17
68	$11\frac{1}{4}$		18
69	$11\frac{7}{8}$		19
70	$12\frac{1}{2}$		20
71	$13\frac{1}{8}$		21
72	$13\frac{3}{4}$		22
73	$14\frac{3}{8}$		23
74	15		24
75	$15\frac{5}{8}$		25
76	$16\frac{1}{4}$		26
77	$16\frac{7}{8}$		27

Code	Statute miles	Yards	Kilometres
24	$1\frac{1}{2}$	2640	2.4
25	$1\frac{9}{16}$	2750	2.5
26	$1\frac{5}{8}$	2860	2.6
27	$1\frac{11}{16}$	2970	2.7
28	$1\frac{3}{4}$	3080	2.8
29	$1\frac{13}{16}$	3190	2.9
30	$1\frac{7}{8}$	3300	3.0
31	$1\frac{15}{16}$	3410	3.1
32	2	3520	3.2
33	$2\frac{1}{16}$	3630	3.3
34	$2\frac{1}{8}$	3740	3.4
35	$2\frac{3}{16}$	3850	3.5
36	$2\frac{1}{4}$	3960	3.6
37	$2\frac{5}{16}$	4070	3.7
38	$2\frac{3}{8}$	4180	3.8
39	$2\frac{7}{16}$	4290	3.9
40	$2\frac{1}{2}$	4400	4.0
41	$2\frac{9}{16}$	4510	4.1
42	$2\frac{5}{8}$	4620	4.2
43	$2\frac{11}{16}$	4730	4.3
44	$2\frac{3}{4}$	4840	4.4
45	$2\frac{13}{16}$	4950	4.5
46	$2\frac{7}{8}$	5060	4.6
47	$2\frac{15}{16}$	5170	4.7
48	3	5280	4.8
49	$3\frac{1}{16}$	5390	4.9
50	$3\frac{1}{8}$	5500	5.0
51	Not specified.		
52	Not specified.		
53	Not specified.		
78	$17\frac{1}{2}$		28
79	$18\frac{1}{8}$		29
80	$18\frac{3}{4}$		30
81	$21\frac{7}{8}$		35
82	25		40
83	$28\frac{1}{8}$		45
84	$31\frac{1}{4}$		50
85	$34\frac{3}{8}$		55
86	$37\frac{1}{2}$		60
87	$40\frac{5}{8}$		65
88	$43\frac{3}{4}$		70
89	Greater than $43\frac{3}{4}$		Greater than 70.
90		Less than 55.	Less than 50 m.
91		55.	50 m.
92	$\frac{1}{8}$	220.	200 m.
93	$\frac{5}{16}$	550.	500 m.
94	$\frac{5}{8}$	1100.	1 km.
95	$1\frac{1}{4}$	2200.	2
96	$2\frac{1}{2}$	4400.	4
97	$6\frac{1}{4}$		10
98	$12\frac{1}{2}$		20
99	$31\frac{1}{4}$ or more.		50 or more.

Notes:
(1) The values given are discrete values (i.e., not ranges). If the observed visibility is between two of the reportable distances as given in the table, the code figure of the lower reportable distance shall be reported.
(2) Only the code figures 00–89 shall be used in reports from land stations.
(3) In reporting visibility at sea the decade 90–99 shall be used.

Table 18
Present Weather (ww)

Code	Description
00	Cloud development NOT observed or NOT observable during past hour.§
01	Clouds generally dissolving or becoming less developed during past hour.§
02	State of sky on the whole unchanged during past hour.§
03	Clouds generally forming or developing during past hour.§
04	Visibility reduced by smoke.
05	Dry haze.
06	Widespread dust in suspension in the air. NOT raised by wind, at time of observation.
07	Dust or sand raised by wind, at time of ob.
08	Well developed dust devil(s) within past hr.
09	Duststorm or sandstorm within sight of or at station during past hr.
10	Light fog.
11	Patches or shallow fog at station. NOT deeper than 6 feet on land.
12	More or less continuous shallow fog at station, NOT deeper than 6 feet on land.
13	Lightning visible, no thunder heard.
14	Precipitation within sight, but NOT reaching the ground at station.
15	Precipitation within sight, reaching ground, but distant from station.
16	Precipitation within sight, reaching the ground, near to but NOT at station.
17	Thunder heard, but no precipitation at the station.
18	Squall(s) within sight during past hour.
19	Funnel cloud(s) within sight during past hr.
20	Drizzle (NOT freezing and NOT falling as showers) during past hr. but NOT at time of ob.
21	Rain (NOT freezing and NOT falling as showers) during past hr. but NOT at time of ob.
22	Snow (NOT falling as showers) during past hr. but NOT at time of ob.
23	Rain and snow (NOT falling as showers) during past hr. but NOT at time of observation.
24	Freezing drizzle or freezing rain (NOT falling as showers) during past hr. but NOT at time of observation.
25	Showers of rain during past hour, but NOT at time of observation.
26	Showers of snow, or of rain and snow, during past hr. but NOT at time of observation.
27	Showers of hail, or of hail and rain, during past hour, but NOT at time of observation.
28	Fog during past hour, but NOT at time of ob.
29	Thunderstorm (with or without precipitation) during past hour, but NOT at time of ob.
30	Slight or moderate duststorm or sandstorm, has decreased during past hour.
31	Slight or moderate duststorm or sandstorm, no appreciable change during past hour.
32	Slight or moderate duststorm or sandstorm, has increased during past hour.
33	Severe duststorm or sandstorm, has decreased during past hour.
34	Severe duststorm or sandstorm, no appreciable change during past hr. hour.
35	Severe duststorm or sandstorm, has increased during past hr.
36	Slight or moderate drifting snow, generally low.
37	Heavy drifting snow, generally low.
38	Slight or moderate drifting snow, generally high.
39	Heavy drifting snow, generally high.
40	Fog at distance at time of ob., but NOT at station during past hour.
41	Fog in patches.
42	Fog, sky discernible, has become thinner during past hour.
43	Fog, sky NOT discernible, has become thinner during past hour.
44	Fog, sky discernible, no appreciable change during past hour.
45	Fog, sky NOT discernible, no appreciable change during past hour.
46	Fog, sky discernible, has begun or become thicker during past hour.
47	Fog, sky NOT discernible, has begun or become thicker during past hour.
48	Fog, depositing rime, sky discernible.
49	Fog, depositing rime, sky NOT discernible.

§ The symbol is not plotted for "ww" when "00" is reported. When "01, 02, or 03" is reported for "ww," the symbol is plotted on the station circle.

Code	Description
50	Intermittent drizzle (NOT freezing) slight at time of observation.
51	Continuous drizzle (NOT freezing) slight at time of observation.
52	Intermittent drizzle (NOT freezing) moderate at time of ob.
53	Continuous drizzle (NOT freezing) moderate at time of ob.
54	Intermittent drizzle (NOT freezing), thick at time of observation.
55	Continuous drizzle (NOT freezing), thick at time of observation.
56	Slight freezing drizzle.
57	Moderate or thick freezing drizzle.
58	Drizzle and rain, slight.
59	Drizzle and rain, moderate or heavy.
60	Intermittent rain (NOT freezing), slight at time of observation.
61	Continuous rain (NOT freezing), slight at time of observation.
62	Intermittent rain (NOT freezing), moderate at time of ob.
63	Continuous rain (NOT freezing), moderate at time of observation.
64	Intermittent rain (NOT freezing), heavy at time of observation.
65	Continuous rain (NOT freezing), heavy at time of observation.
66	Slight freezing rain.
67	Moderate or heavy freezing rain.
68	Rain or drizzle and snow, slight.
69	Rain or drizzle and snow, mod., or heavy.
70	Intermittent fall of snow flakes, slight at time of observation.
71	Continuous fall of snowflakes, slight at time of observation.
72	Intermittent fall of snow flakes, moderate at time of observation.
73	Continuous fall of snowflakes, moderate time of observation.
74	Intermittent fall of snow flakes, heavy at time of observation.
75	Continuous fall of snowflakes, heavy at time of observation.
76	Ice needles (with or without fog).
77	Granular snow (with or without fog).
78	Isolated starlike snow crystals (with or without fog).
79	Ice pellets (sleet, U.S. definition).
80	Slight rain shower(s).
81	Moderate or heavy rain shower(s).
82	Violent rain shower(s).
83	Slight shower(s) of rain and snow mixed.
84	Moderate or heavy shower(s) of rain and snow mixed.
85	Slight snow shower(s).
86	Moderate or heavy snow shower(s).
87	Slight shower(s) of soft or small hail with or without rain and snow mixed.
88	Moderate or heavy shower(s) of soft or small hail with or without rain and snow mixed.
89	Slight shower(s) of hail†, with or without rain or rain and snow mixed, not associated with thunder.
90	Moderate or heavy shower(s) of hail†, with or without rain or rain and snow mixed, not associated with thunder.
91	Slight rain at time of ob., thunderstorm during past hour, but NOT at time of observation.
92	Moderate or heavy rain at time of ob.; thunderstorm during past hour, but NOT at time of observation.
93	Slight snow or rain and snow mixed or hail† at time of ob.; thunderstorm during past hour, but NOT at time of observation.
94	Mod. or heavy snow, or rain and snow mixed or hail† at time of ob.; thunderstorm during past hour, but NOT at time of observation.
95	Slight or mod. thunderstorm without hail†, but with rain and or snow at time of observation.
96	Slight or mod. thunderstorm with hail† at time of observation.
97	Heavy thunderstorm, without hail†, but with rain and or snow at time of observation.
98	Thunderstorm combined with duststorm or sandstorm at time of ob.
99	Heavy thunderstorm with hail† at time of ob.

† Refers to "hail" only.   †† Refers to "soft hail," "small hail," and "hail."

Table 19
Past Weather (W)

Code Number	W	Past Weather (W)
0		Clear or few clouds. Covering 1/2 or less of sky during the entire period. (Not plotted.)
1		Partly cloudy. Covering more than 1/2 for part of period; 1/2 or less for part of same period. (Not plotted.)
2		Cloudy, broken clouds, overcast. Cloud covering more than 1/2 during the entire period. (Not plotted.)
3	⌐⌐ or ⊣⊢	Sandstorm, duststorm, blowing or drifting snow.
4	≡	Fog, ice fog, thick haze, or thick smoke.
5	,	Drizzle.
6	●	Rain.
7	✳	Snow, rain and snow mixed, or ice pellets (sleet).
8	▽	Shower or showers.
9	⃢	Thunderstorm, with or without precipitation.

Note: The period of time for reporting past weather (W) is the *6 hr* preceding the actual time of observation for the *primary synoptic* (6-hourly) reports of 0000, 0600, 1200, and 1800 GMT. However, past weather (W) covers the *3 hr* preceding the actual time of observation for the *intermediate synoptic* (3-hourly) reports of 0300, 0900, 1500, and 2100 GMT.

Table 20
Height of Clouds[1] (h)

h Code Number	Height in Feet	Approximate Height in Meters
0	0–149	0–49
1	150–299	50–99
2	300–599	100–199
3	600–999	200–299
4	1000–1999	300–599
5	2000–3499	600–999
6	3500–4999	1000–1499
7	5000–6499	1500–1999
8	6500–7999	2000–2499
9	8000 or higher, or no clouds	2500 or higher, or no clouds

[1] Height of clouds is the distance between the ground and the base of the cloud (the ceiling).

Table 21
Alphabetical List of Cloud Abbreviations

Ac	Altocumulus	Cu	Cumulus
As	Altostratus	Fc	Fractocumulus
Cb	Cumulonimbus	Fs	Fractostratus
Cc	Cirrocumulus	Ns	Nimbostratus
Ci	Cirrus	Sc	Stratocumulus
Cs	Cirrostratus	St	Stratus

Table 22
Low Clouds (C_L)

Code No.	C_L	Low Clouds
1		Fair weather Cu; little vertical development.
2		Cu of moderate to strong vertical development with or without *Cu*, or Sc; bases at same level.
3		Cb, tops lack clear outlines but no Ci or anvil top; with or without Cu, Sc, St.
4		Sc formed by the spreading out of Cu; Cu may be present.
5		Sc not formed by the spreading out of Cu.
6		St or Fs or both, but no Fs of bad weather; St in a generally continuous layer.
7		Fs and/or Fc of bad weather; usually below As or Ns.
8		Cu and Sc with bases at different levels; Sc is not formed by the spreading out of Cu.
9		Cb with cirriform top, often anvil-shaped; with or without Cu, Sc, Fc, Fs, other Cb.
0		No C_L clouds; no Sc, St, Cu, or Cb.

Table 23
Middle Clouds (C_M)

Code No.	C_M	Middle Clouds
1		As, mostly semitransparent, thin.
2		As, mostly dense enough to hide sun or moon; or Ns.
3		Ac, mostly semitransparent, thin; cloud elements at one level, changing slowly.
4		Ac in patches, often lenticular, mostly semitransparent, at many levels, changing.
5		Ac in bans or one or more layers, invading the sky and usually thickening.
6		Ac formed from the spreading out of Cu or Cb.
7		Ac in two or more layers, not invading sky; or, thick Ac; or, Ac with As and/or Ns.
8		Ac with sproutings in form of small towers or Ac with appearance of cumuliform tufts.
9		Ac of a chaotic sky, generally at several levels.
0		No C_M clouds; no Ac, As, or Ns.

Table 24
High Clouds (C_H)

Code No.	C_H	High Clouds
1		Ci filaments, hooks, and strands; not increasing; scattered.
2		Dense Ci in patches or entangled sheaves; Ci with small turrets, tufts.
3		Dense Ci often in the form of an anvil as remains of upper parts of Cb.
4		Ci in form of hooks and/or filaments; invading the sky and thickening.
5		Ci and Cs or Cs alone; invading the sky and thickening; higher than 45° above horizon.
6		Same as above except that the continuous veil extends lower than 45° above horizon.
7		Veil of Cs covering the entire sky.
8		Cs not progressively invading the sky and not covering the entire sky.
9		Cc alone or Cc with Ci and/or Cs; but Cc is predominant.
0		No C_H clouds; no Ci, Cc, or Cs.

Table 25
Pressure Tendency (a)

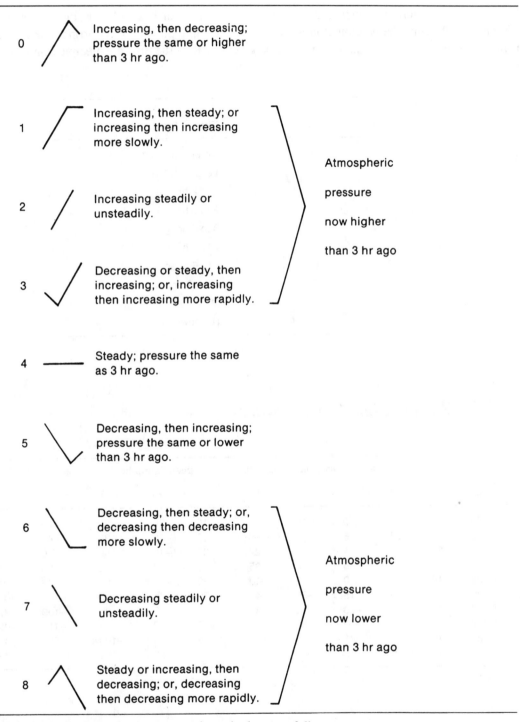

0	Increasing, then decreasing; pressure the same or higher than 3 hr ago.	
1	Increasing, then steady; or increasing then increasing more slowly.	Atmospheric pressure now higher than 3 hr ago
2	Increasing steadily or unsteadily.	
3	Decreasing or steady, then increasing; or, increasing then increasing more rapidly.	
4	Steady; pressure the same as 3 hr ago.	
5	Decreasing, then increasing; pressure the same or lower than 3 hr ago.	
6	Decreasing, then steady; or, decreasing then decreasing more slowly.	Atmospheric pressure now lower than 3 hr ago
7	Decreasing steadily or unsteadily.	
8	Steady or increasing, then decreasing; or, decreasing then decreasing more rapidly.	

Note: On marine radiofacsimile charts the pressure tendency is shown as follows:

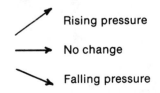

Rising pressure

No change

Falling pressure

Table 26
Time of Precipitation (R_t)

When the precipitation *is* occurring at the time of observation or has ended during the preceeding hour, the time give for R_t is the time the precipitation *began*. When precipitation is *not* occurring at the time of observation and has not occurred in the preceeding hour, the time given for R_t is the time the precipitation *ended.*

Code Number	Time of Precipitation
0	No precipitation
1	Less than 1 hr ago
2	1 to 2 hr ago
3	2 to 3 hr ago
4	3 to 4 hr ago
5	4 to 5 hr ago
6	5 to 6 hr ago
7	6 to 12 hr ago
8	More than 12 hr ago
9	Unknown

Table 27
Wind-Chill Equivalent Temperatures

MPH	Dry-Bulb Temperatures (in degrees Fahrenheit)											
	50	40	30	20	10	0	−10	−20	−30	−40	−50	−60
0	50	40	30	20	10	0	−10	−20	−30	−40	−50	−60
5	48	37	27	16	6	−5	−15	−26	−36	−47	−57	−68
10	40	28	16	4	−9	−22	−33	−46	−58	−70	−83	−95
15	36	23	9	−5	−18	−35	−45	−58	−72	−85	−99	−112
20	32	19	4	−10	−25	−40	−53	−67	−82	−96	−110	−124
25	30	16	0	−15	−29	−45	−59	−74	−88	−104	−118	−133
30	28	13	−2	−18	−33	−49	−63	−79	−94	−109	−125	−140
35	27	11	−4	−20	−35	−52	−67	−82	−98	−113	−129	−145
40	26	10	−6	−21	−37	−53	−69	−85	−100	−116	−132	−148
45	26	10	−6	−22	−38	−54	−70	−85	−101	−117	−132	−148

Table 28
Selected Climate Data

Station	Elevation		Jan	Feb	Mar	Apr	May	Jun	Jul	Aug	Sep	Oct	Nov	Dec	Year
Austin,		T	50	53	61	69	75	82	85	85	80	70	60	52	69
Texas	597 ft	P	1.6	2.3	1.8	2.9	4.3	3.5	1.9	1.9	3.3	3.5	2.1	1.9	31.1
Evansville,		T	27	31	41	52	63	72	76	73	67	55	43	31	53
Indiana	380 ft	P	2.8	2.5	3.6	3.6	4.0	3.9	4.3	3.4	2.9	2.6	3.3	3.3	40.2
Fargo,		T	6	12	25	43	56	66	71	69	58	46	28	13	41
North Dakota	900 ft	P	.6	.6	.9	1.7	2.3	3.0	3.1	2.4	1.8	1.5	.8	.6	19.3
Havana,		T	70	72	73	76	79	81	82	82	80	78	75	72	77
Cuba	161 ft	P	2.7	2.3	1.8	2.8	4.5	7.2	5.0	6.0	6.7	7.4	3.1	2.2	51.7
Haverhill,		T	28	29	37	48	60	69	74	72	64	54	43	31	51
Massachusetts	60 ft	P	3.7	2.9	3.8	3.4	3.2	3.1	3.7	2.9	3.7	3.0	3.8	3.3	40.5
Jacksonville,		T	55	58	63	69	75	80	82	82	78	71	62	56	69
Florida	26 ft	P	2.8	3.0	2.9	2.4	4.0	5.3	6.7	5.8	7.4	4.5	2.0	3.0	49.8
Juneau,		T	27	30	34	41	48	54	57	55	50	43	35	31	42
Alaska	72 ft	P	6.9	5.3	5.1	5.3	5.2	3.7	5.1	7.4	10.7	10.3	8.3	7.4	80.7
Lima,		T	71	73	73	70	66	62	61	61	61	62	66	70	66
Peru	512 ft	P	0.02	0.01	0.02	0.03	0.10	0.24	0.35	0.41	0.39	0.19	0.10	0.04	1.90
Moscow,		T	12	15	23	38	53	62	66	63	52	40	28	17	39
Russia	525 ft	P	1.1	0.9	1.2	1.5	1.9	2.0	2.8	2.9	2.2	1.4	1.6	1.5	21.0
New York,		T	31	31	38	49	61	69	74	73	67	56	44	35	52
New York	132 ft	P	3.7	3.8	3.6	3.2	3.2	3.3	4.2	4.3	3.4	3.5	3.0	3.6	42.8
Quito,		T	55	55	55	55	55	55	55	55	55	55	54	55	55
Ecuador	9350 ft	P	3.2	3.9	4.8	7.0	4.6	1.5	1.1	2.2	2.6	3.9	4.0	3.6	42.3
Seattle,		T	40	41	45	49	55	59	63	63	58	51	46	42	51
Washington	400 ft	P	4.9	3.9	3.1	2.4	1.9	1.3	0.6	0.7	1.8	2.8	5.0	5.6	34.0
Verkhoyansk,		T	−59	−47	−24	7	35	55	60	50	36	5	−34	−53	3
Russia	330 ft	P	0.2	0.2	0.1	0.2	0.3	0.9	1.1	1.0	0.5	0.3	0.3	0.2	5.3
Cherrapunji,		T	53	55	62	65	66	68	68	69	69	66	60	55	63
India	4309 ft	P	0.5	2.7	9.4	28.2	46.3	95.9	99.5	79.8	38.1	21.2	3.2	0.3	425.1
Bergen,		T	35	35	37	42	49	54	58	57	52	45	39	36	45
Norway	146 ft	P	8.7	5.9	5.5	4.4	4.2	4.1	4.3	7.2	7.8	8.7	7.7	8.1	76.6

Table 29
Hurricanes Andrew and Bob

Hurricane Andrew, August 1992

Day	Time (GMT)	Position Lat.	Long.	Pressure (mb)	Wind (kt)	Speed (MPH)
16	1800	10.8	35.5	1010	25	
17	0000	11.2	37.4	1009	30	
	0600	11.7	39.6	1008	30	
	1200	12.3	42.0	1006	35	
	1800	13.1	44.2	1003	35	
18	0000	13.6	46.2	1002	40	
	0600	14.1	48.0	1001	45	
	1200	14.6	49.9	1000	45	
	1800	15.4	51.8	1000	45	
19	0000	16.3	53.5	1001	.45	
	0600	17.2	55.3	1002	45	
	1200	18.0	56.9	1005	45	
	1800	18.8	58.3	1007	45	
20	0000	19.8	59.3	1011	40	
	0600	20.7	60.0	1013	40	
	1200	21.7	60.7	1015	40	
	1800	22.5	61.5	1014	40	
21	0000	23.2	62.4	1014	45	
	0600	23.9	63.3	1010	45	
	1200	24.4	64.2	1007	50	
	1800	24.8	64.9	1004	50	
22	0000	25.3	65.9	1000	55	
	0600	25.6	67.0	994	60	
	1200	25.8	68.3	981	70	
	1800	25.7	69.7	969	80	
23	0000	25.6	71.1	961	90	
	0600	25.5	72.5	947	105	
	1200	25.4	74.2	933	120	
	1800	25.4	75.8	922	135	
24	0000	25.4	77.5	930	125	
	0600	25.4	79.3	937	120	
	1200	25.6	81.2	951	110	
	1800	25.8	83.1	947	115	
25	0000	26.2	85.0	943	115	
	0600	26.6	86.7	948	115	
	1200	27.2	88.2	946	115	
	1800	27.8	89.6	941	120	
26	0000	28.5	90.5	937	120	
	0600	29.2	91.3	955	115	
	1200	30.1	91.7	973	80	
	1800	30.9	91.6	991	50	
27	0000	31.5	91.1	995	35	
	0600	32.1	90.5	997	30	
	1200	32.8	89.6	998	30	
	1800	33.6	88.4	999	25	
28	0000	34.4	86.7	1000	20	
	0600	35.4	84.0	1000	20	

Hurricane Bob, August 1991

Day	Time (GMT)	Position Lat.	Long.	Pressure (mb)	Wind (kt)	Speed (MPH)
16	0000	25.6	74.3	1014	25	
	0600	25.7	74.9	1012	25	
	1200	25.9	75.4	1010	30	
	1800	26.4	75.8	1005	35	
17	0000	27.1	76.2	1003	40	
	0600	27.8	76.5	998	45	
	1200	28.4	76.9	996	55	
	1800	29.0	77.1	986	65	
18	0000	29.7	77.0	980	70	
	0600	30.5	76.9	979	75	
	1200	31.5	76.6	974	80	
	1800	33.0	76.1	965	85	
19	0000	34.6	75.3	957	95	
	0600	36.5	74.5	950	100	
	1200	38.9	73.0	953	95	
	1800	41.4	71.4	964	85	
20	0000	43.8	69.6	977	60	
	0600	45.6	67.6	987	50	
	1200	47.0	65.5	998	45	
	1800	48.4	61.9	1003	40	
21	0000	49.8	58.3	1008	40	
	0600	50.9	54.9	1008	40	
	1200	51.6	51.4	1009	35	
	1800	51.9	47.3	1009	30	
22	0000	51.9	42.8	1004	30	
	0600	51.5	38.3	1002	35	
	1200	50.7	34.1	994	40	
	1800	49.3	30.3	992	40	
23	0000	47.7	26.9	992	40	
	0600	46.3	23.9	996	40	
	1200	45.3	21.4	1000	35	
	1800	44.2	19.9	1004	30	
24	0000	43.1	19.4	1006	25	
	0600	42.4	19.1	1008	25	
	1200	42.2	18.6	1009	25	
	1800	42.1	18.1	1009	25	
25	0000	41.9	17.9	1009	25	
	0600	41.7	17.8	1010	25	
	1200	41.3	17.6	1010	25	
	1800	40.9	17.3	1010	25	
26	0000	40.5	16.8	1010	25	
	0600	40.2	16.0	1010	25	
	1200	40.0	15.2	1012	20	
	1800	39.9	14.4	1012	20	
27	0000	39.9	13.8	1014	20	
	0600	40.0	13.1	1014	20	
	1200	40.0	12.4	1014	20	
	1800	40.0	11.8	1014	20	
28	0000	40.0	11.3	1015	15	
	0600	40.0	10.9	1015	15	
	1200	40.0	10.5	1014	15	
	1800	40.0	10.1	1014	10	
29	0000	40.0	9.9	1015	10	

appendix **B** ————————————————————

EXTRA WORK MAPS

name   section   date

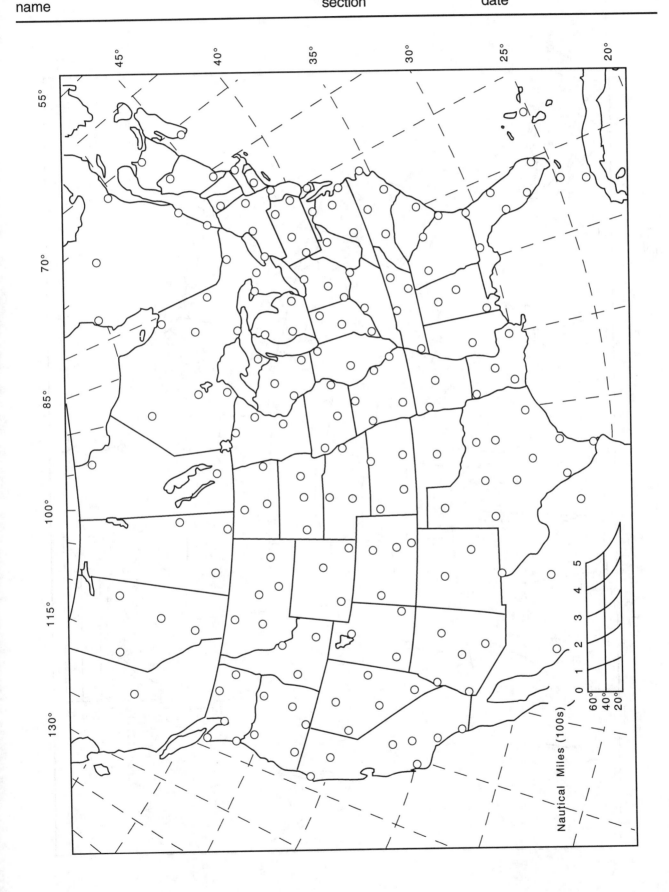

name   section   date

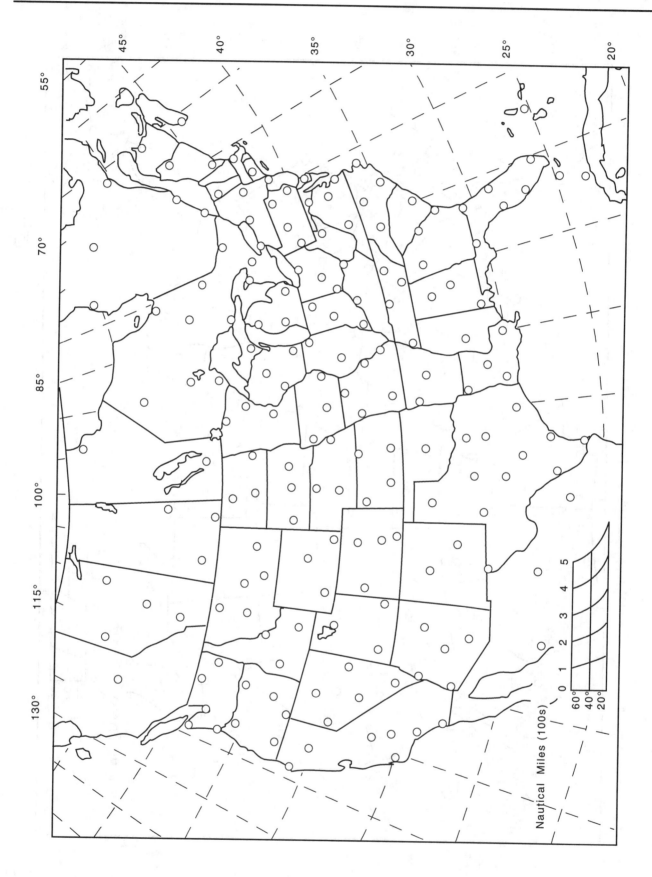

name   section   date

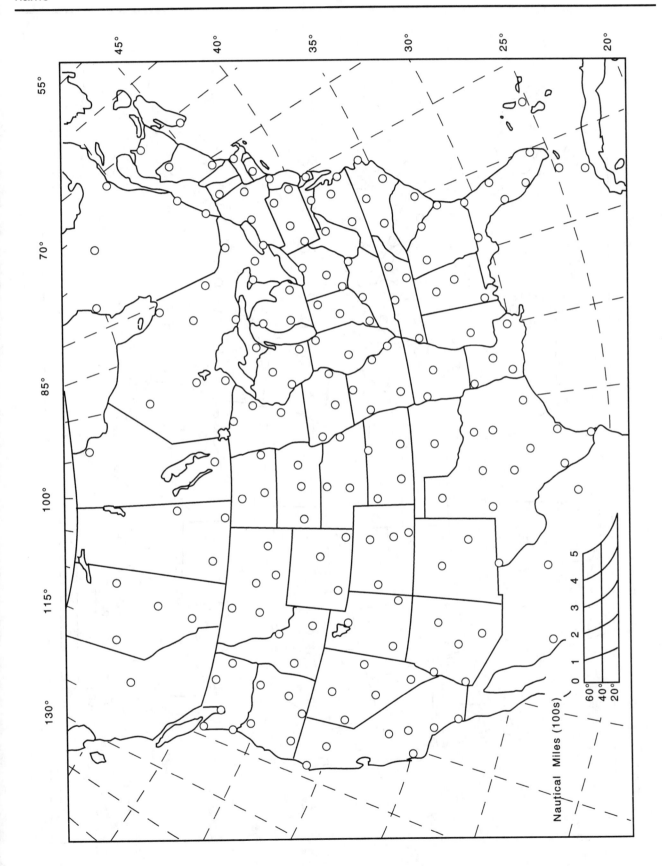

name   section   date

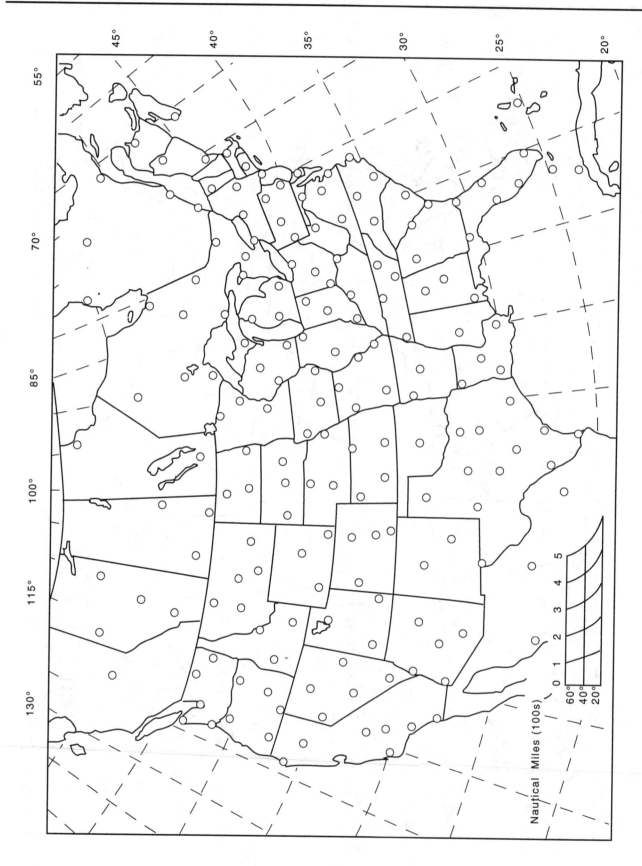

name section date

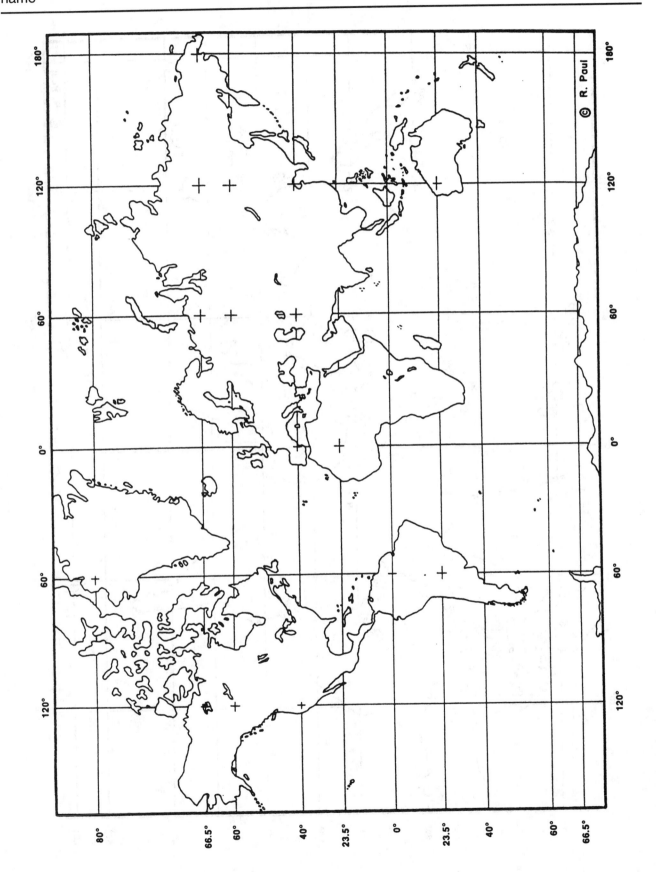

name section date

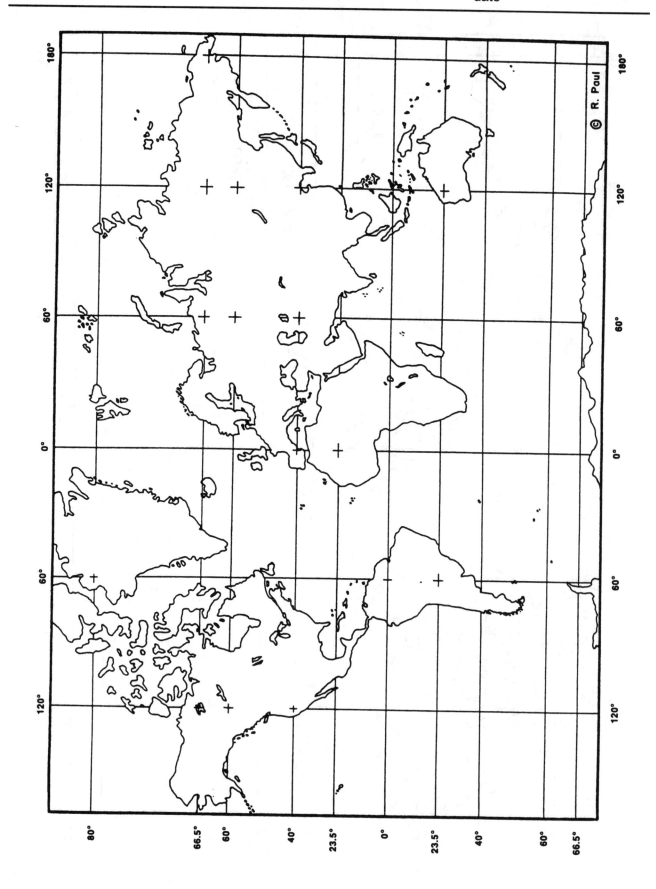

name   section   date

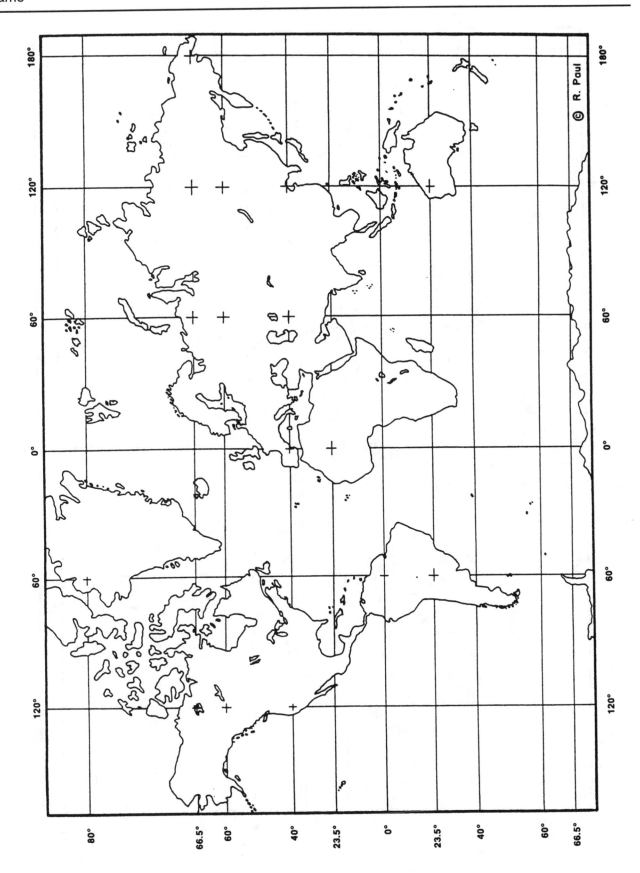

© R. Paul

name   section   date

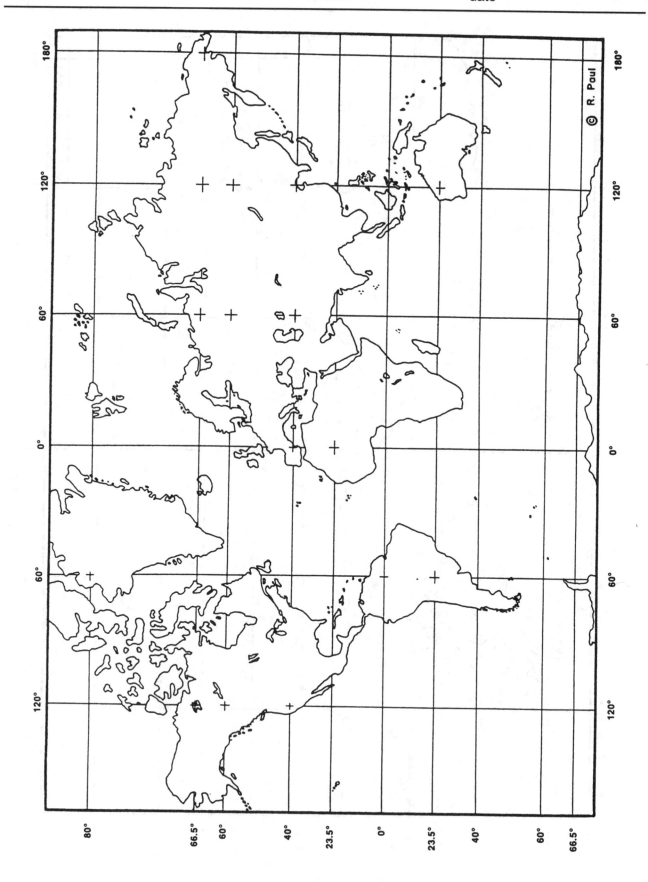

name   section   date

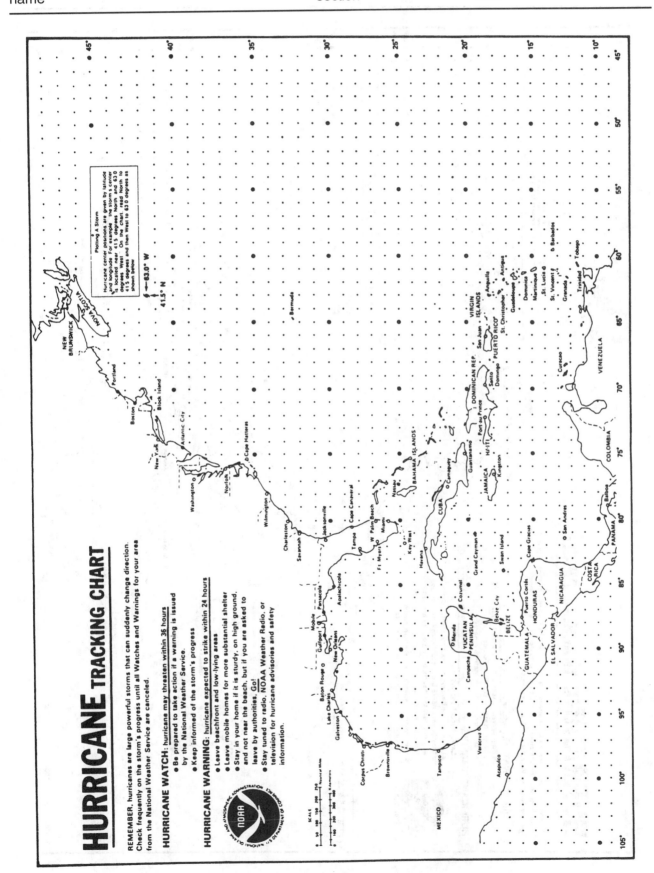

name   section   date

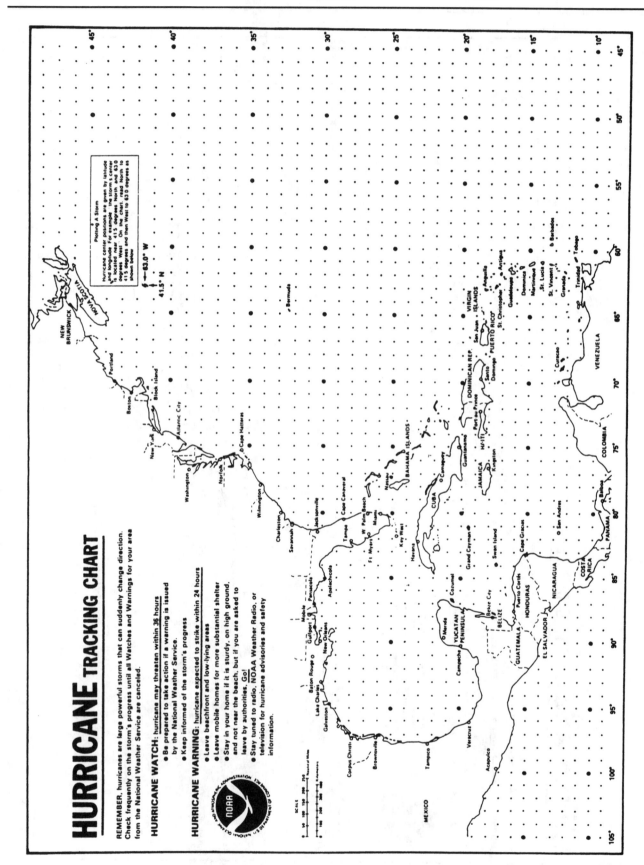

name   section   date

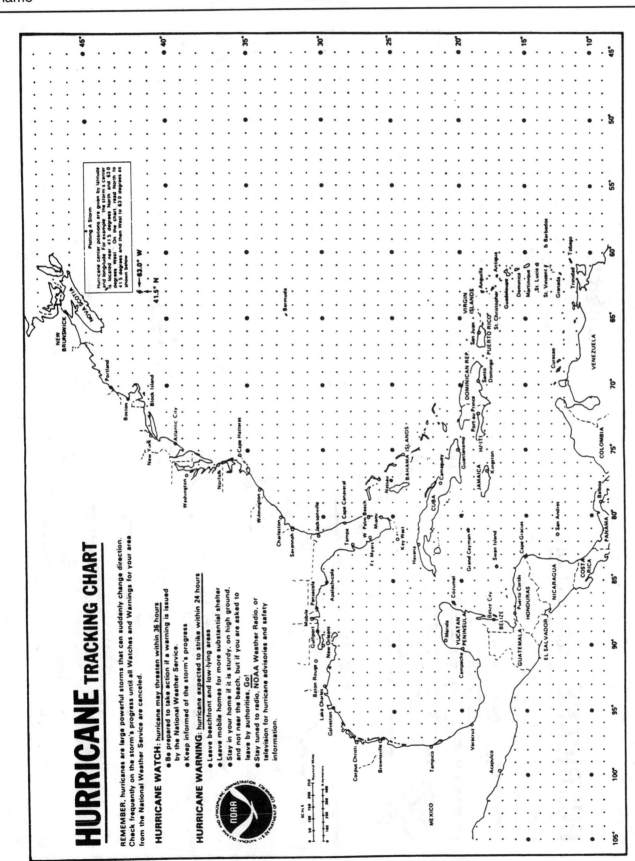

name   section   date

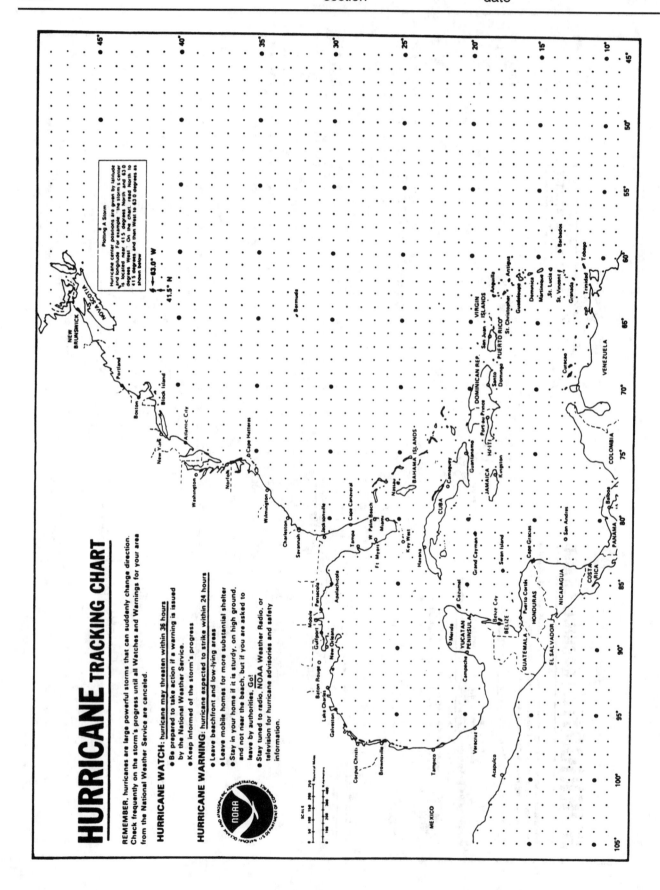

name   section   date

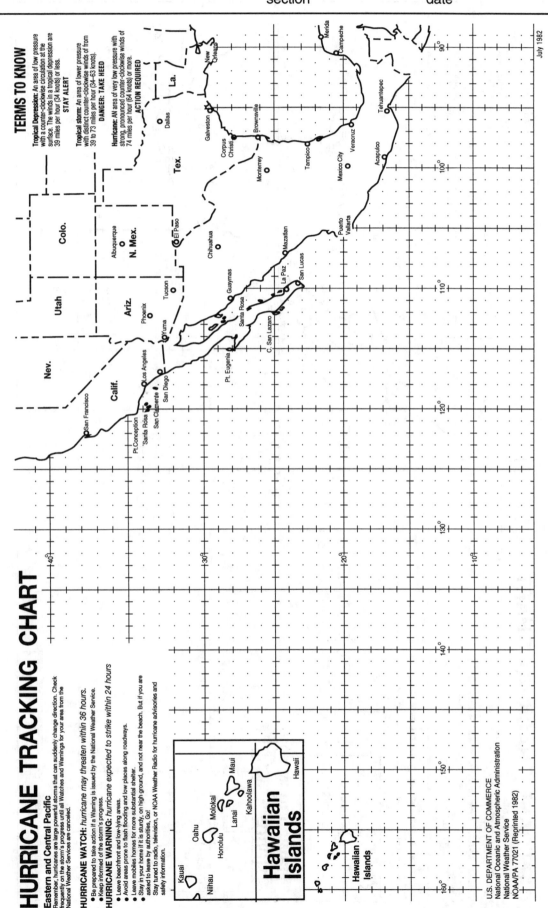

HURRICANE TRACKING CHART

Eastern and Central Pacific

Remember, hurricanes are large powerful storms that can suddenly change direction. Check frequently on the storm's progress until all Watches and Warnings for your area from the National Weather Services are canceled.

HURRICANE WATCH: *hurricane may threaten within 36 hours.*
• Be prepared to take action if a Warning is issued by the National Weather Service.
• Keep informed of the storm's progress.

HURRICANE WARNING: *hurricane expected to strike within 24 hours*
• Leave beachfront and low-lying areas.
• Avoid areas prone to flash flooding and low places along roadways.
• Leave mobiles homes for more substantial shelter.
• Stay in your home if it is sturdy, on high ground, and not near the beach. But if you are asked to leave by authorities, Go!
  Stay tuned to radio, television, or NOAA Weather Radio for hurricane advisories and safety information.

TERMS TO KNOW

Tropical Depression: An area of low pressure with a counter-clockwise circulation at the surface. The winds in a tropical depression are 39 miles per hour (34 knots) or less.
STAY ALERT

Tropical storm: An area of lower pressure with distinct counter-clockwise winds of from 39 to 73 miles per hour (34–63 knots).
DANGER: TAKE HEED

Hurricane: An area of very low pressure with strong, pronounced counter-clockwise winds of 74 miles per hour (64 knots) or more.
ACTION REQUIRED

July 1982

U.S. DEPARTMENT OF COMMERCE
National Oceanic and Atmospheric Administration
National Weather Service
NOAA/PA 77021 (Reprinted 1982)

Hawaiian Islands

Hawaiian Islands

Kauai
Niihau
Oahu
Honolulu
Molokai
Lanai Maui
Kahoolawa
Hawaii

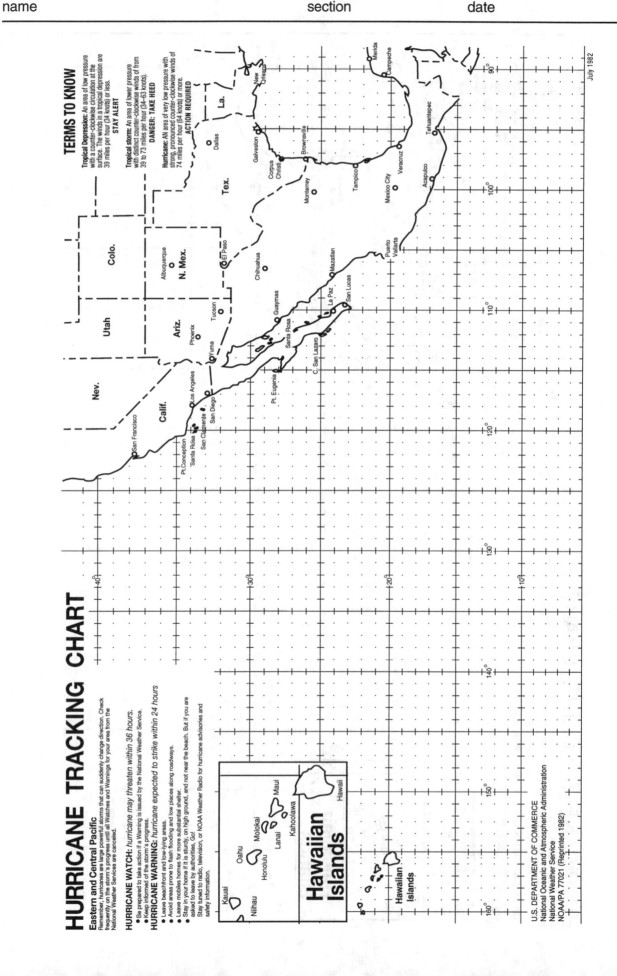

HURRICANE TRACKING CHART

Eastern and Central Pacific

Remember, hurricanes are large powerful storms that can suddenly change direction. Check frequently on the storm's progress until all Watches and Warnings for your area from the National Weather Services are canceled.

HURRICANE WATCH: *hurricane may threaten within 36 hours.*
- Be prepared to take action if a Warning is issued by the National Weather Service.
- Keep informed of the storm's progress.

HURRICANE WARNING: *hurricane expected to strike within 24 hours*
- Leave beachfront and low-lying areas.
- Avoid areas prone to flash flooding and low places along roadways.
- Leave mobiles homes for more substantial shelter.
- Stay in your home if it is sturdy, on high ground, and not near the beach. But if you are asked to leave by authorities, Go! Stay tuned to radio, television, or NOAA Weather Radio for hurricane advisories and safety information.

TERMS TO KNOW

Tropical Depression: An area of low pressure with a counter-clockwise circulation at the surface. The winds in a tropical depression are 39 miles per hour (34 knots) or less.
STAY ALERT

Tropical storm: An area of lower pressure with distinct counter-clockwise winds of from 39 to 73 miles per hour (34-63 knots).
DANGER: TAKE HEED

Hurricane: AN area of very low pressure with strong, pronounced counter-clockwise winds of 74 miles per hour (64 knots) or more.
ACTION REQUIRED

Hawaiian Islands

Kauai
Niihau
Oahu
Honolulu
Molokai
Lanai
Maui
Kahoolawa
Hawaii

Hawaiian Islands

Hawaiian Islands

July 1982

U.S. DEPARTMENT OF COMMERCE
National Oceanic and Atmospheric Administration
National Weather Service
NOAA/PA 77021 (Reprinted 1982)

name   section   date

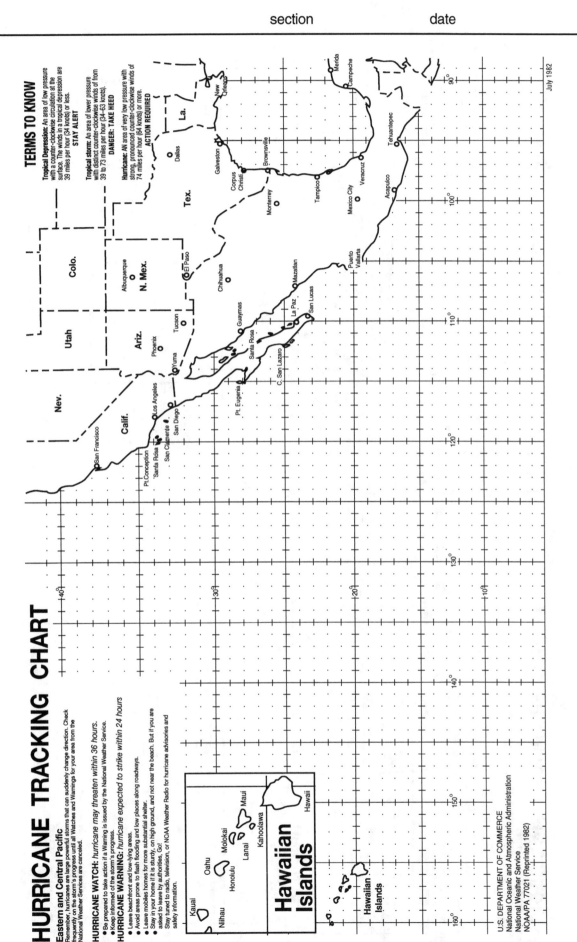

HURRICANE TRACKING CHART

Eastern and Central Pacific

Remember, hurricanes are large powerful storms that can suddenly change direction. Check frequently on the storm's progress until all Watches and Warnings for your area from the National Weather Services are canceled.

HURRICANE WATCH: *hurricane may threaten within 36 hours.*
● Be prepared to take action if a Warning is issued by the National Weather Service.
● Keep informed of the storm's progress.

HURRICANE WARNING: *hurricane expected to strike within 24 hours.*
● Leave beachfront and low-lying areas.
● Avoid areas prone to flash flooding and low places along roadways.
● Leave mobiles homes for more substantial shelter.
● Stay in your home if it is sturdy, on high ground, and not near the beach. But if you are asked to leave by authorities, Go!
● Stay tuned to radio, television, or NOAA Weather Radio for hurricane advisories and safety information.

TERMS TO KNOW

Tropical Depression: An area of low pressure with a counter-clockwise circulation at the surface. The winds in a tropical depression are 39 miles per hour (34 knots) or less.
STAY ALERT

Tropical storm: An area of lower pressure with distinct counter-clockwise winds of from 39 to 73 miles per hour (34–63 knots).
DANGER: TAKE HEED

Hurricane: An area of very low pressure with strong, pronounced counter-clockwise winds of 74 miles per hour (64 knots) or more.
ACTION REQUIRED

July 1982

Hawaiian Islands

U.S. DEPARTMENT OF COMMERCE
National Oceanic and Atmospheric Administration
National Weather Service
NOAA/PA 77021 (Reprinted 1982)

name   section   date

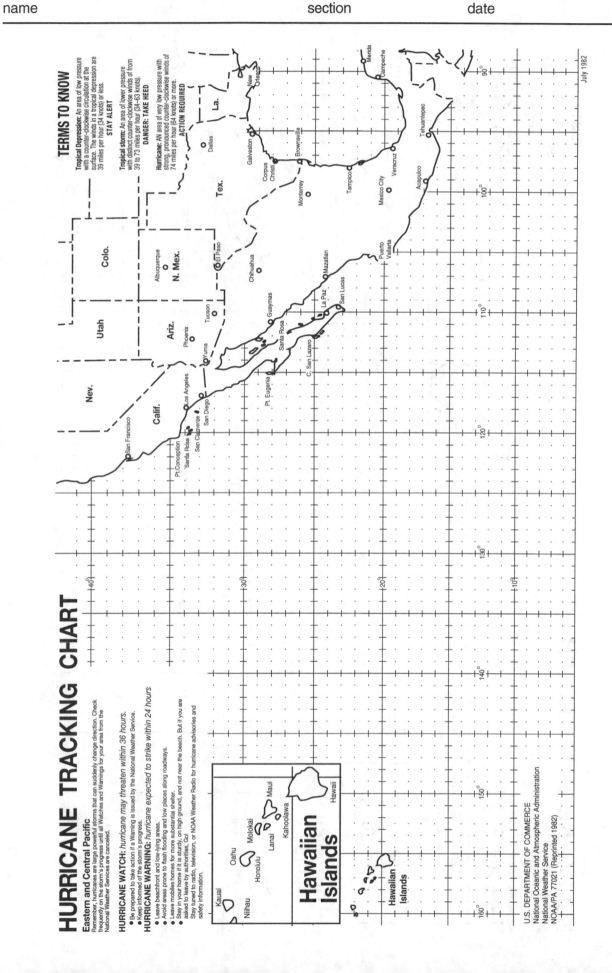

HURRICANE TRACKING CHART

Eastern and Central Pacific

Remember, hurricanes are large powerful storms that can suddenly change direction. Check frequently on the storm's progress until all Watches and Warnings for your area from the National Weather Services are cancelled.

HURRICANE WATCH: *hurricane may threaten within 36 hours.*
• Be prepared to take action if a Warning is issued by the National Weather Service.
• Keep informed of the storm's progress.

HURRICANE WARNING: *hurricane expected to strike within 24 hours*
• Leave beachfront and low-lying areas.
• Avoid areas prone to flash flooding and low places along roadways.
• Leave mobile homes for more substantial shelter.
• Stay in your home if it is sturdy, on high ground, and not near the beach. But if you are asked to leave by authorities, Go!
Stay tuned to radio, television, or NOAA Weather Radio for hurricane advisories and safety information.

TERMS TO KNOW

Tropical Depression: An area of low pressure with a counter-clockwise circulation at the surface. The winds in a tropical depression are 39 miles per hour (34 knots) or less.
STAY ALERT

Tropical storm: An area of lower pressure with distinct counter-clockwise winds of from 39 to 73 miles per hour (34–63 knots).
DANGER: TAKE HEED

Hurricane: AN area of very low pressure with strong, pronounced counter-clockwise winds of 74 miles per hour (64 knots) or more.
ACTION REQUIRED

Hawaiian Islands

U.S. DEPARTMENT OF COMMERCE
National Oceanic and Atmospheric Administration
National Weather Service
NOAA/PA 77021 (Reprinted 1982)

July 1982

NOTES

NOTES

NOTES

NOTES